CALENDAR COMPANIONS

For Fall

written by
Susanne Glover
and
Georgeann Grewe

illustrated by Georgeann Grewe

Cover by Gary Mohrmann

Copyright © Good Apple, Inc., 1984

GOOD APPLE, INC.
BOX 299
CARTHAGE, ILLINOIS 62321-0299

Copyright © Good Apple, Inc., 1984
ISBN No. 0-86653-200-5
Printing No.

GOOD APPLE, INC.
BOX 299
CARTHAGE, ILLINOIS 62321-0299

To Dad and Jeremy Adam

With love,
Mom

TABLE OF CONTENTS

SEPTEMBER

Teacher Tips

SEPTEMBER (page 1)
*   Use as a coloring sheet.
*   Use as a cover for a September booklet of work sheets or projects.

CALENDAR (page 4)
*   Add numbers for dates, **Calendar Creations** information (page 5), and/or pictures in appropriate boxes.
*   List birthdays of classmates.
*   Use as a monthly weather guide.
*   Assign research for gifted children to create their own calendar events.

CALENDAR CREATIONS (page 5)
*   Allow students to research topics and report findings to class.
*   Announce events in opening exercises each day.

WE "FACE" THE NEW YEAR (pages 6-8)
*   Make this bulletin board to display finished art pictures (faces) of students in the class. Use this bulletin board for September or January as the new year begins.

PUR-R-FECT PENMANSHIP (page 11)
*   Read and review the poem orally with the class, discussing format, rhyme, capital letters, and punctuation before assigning children to copy the poem in their best writing.

WORD WIZARD (page 12)
*   Use the words as a spelling list for the month.
*   Assign topics for research projects.
*   Use the words for **Back-to-School Bingo**. (page 13)

LETTER OUTLINE page 15)
*   Give children this form to write home about their progress.

    Dear Mom and Dad,

    Here is my work for the month of September.

    Please look at it so you will see how I am

    progressing . . . .

SEPTEMBER CINQUAINS--POETRY POINTERS (page 17)
*   Review the poetic form for cinquains. Read and discuss the cinquains presented. Assist children in writing cinquains of their own.

A TASK TO TACKLE (page 18)
*   Write math problems suitable to your grade level in each of the footballs and helmets to use as a beginning-of-the-year diagnostic math test, as a review or as a supplement.
*   Write math facts on the helmets and the answers on the footballs to use as flash cards or seatwork review.
*   Write reading, social studies, or science vocabulary words on the helmets and footballs and the answers or definitions on the backs.

TOUCHDOWNS (page 19)

* Review the concept of bar graphs and keys with the class before assigning this graph to the children for completion.

MINI UNIT--SCHOOL SURVIVAL KIT (page 21)

This unit is designed as a packet for students to use independently the first day of school so that the teacher can complete paper work and information about the class. Although numerous activities for all content areas are presented, select those items appropriate for your grade level. Be sure to give complete instructions before assigning tasks to children so that you may proceed without many interruptions. Some preparation will be necessary. Our suggestions include:

1. **My School Box** -- Use this as a cover/coloring sheet which children will glue to the outside of a manila folder that will contain all completed activities (page 21).
2. **A Sharp Class** -- Have this bulletin board on display so that the children can complete **My Personalized Pencil** and attach their pencils to the bulletin board as they are completed (pages 22-24).
3. **Name Tags** -- Complete these before school begins so children can be identified quickly. Record student bus numbers on the buses if necessary (page 25).
4. **Bookmarks** -- Duplicate these on oaktag and let students color one or two (page 26).
5. **School Bus/Story** -- Provide each child with a copy of both pages. As stories are completed, the bus can be assembled as illustrated and either displayed in the room or added to the folder (pages 27-28).
6. **Fact Pack** -- Give each child a small envelope so that he can complete this math activity. Have each child write multiplication facts on the fronts of the crayons and write the answers on the backs. Vary the activity for addition or subtraction facts. You may want each child to complete a different set of facts so that you will have a complete set for the class to use at a station (pages 29-30).
7. **Measure Up** -- Let students cut out the ruler to complete the math calculations on the page (page 31).
8. **Don't Get Stuck** -- Have students copy the weekly spelling list or **Word Wizard** list and complete the story activity at the bottom of the page (page 32).

Slight preparations may be necessary as the activities are adapted to the needs of your classroom; supplement the materials provided with those of your own!

SEPTEMBER

Calendar Creations

SEPTEMBER:

1 Edgar Rice Burroughs' birthday

3 Revolutionary War officially ended

5 First Labor Day parade in U.S.

6 Jane Addams' birthday

7 Grandma Moses' (Anna Mary Robertson) birthday
Queen Elizabeth 1 of England's birthday

10 Elias Howe given patent for sewing machine

13 Walter Reed's birthday

15 Old People's Day in Japan

16 Louis XIV's birthday

17 U.S. Constitution signed

20 Alexander the Great's birthday

21 First daily newspaper published
(**Pennsylvania Packet and Daily Advertiser**)

23 Autumn begins

24 John Marshall's birthday

25 Vasco de Balboa discoverd the Pacific Ocean
First transoceanic telephone cable established between New
York and London

26 Melissa Sue Anderson's birthday
Good Neighbor Day

27 Samuel Adams' birthday

28 Confucius' birthday

YOU WILL NEED:

1. Yellow background
2. Black letters for title
3. Large paper plates (one per child)
4. Boy and girl patterns (pages 7-8)
5. Yarn, felt, material, construction paper for 3-D effect (optional)

DIRECTIONS:

Give each student a paper plate and basic patterns. Write names of students on bow or collar or just write initials as in a monogram. Attach yarn, cotton, paper chains for hair or simply use construction paper. Patterns may not be necessary for older children.

Basic Boy Pattern

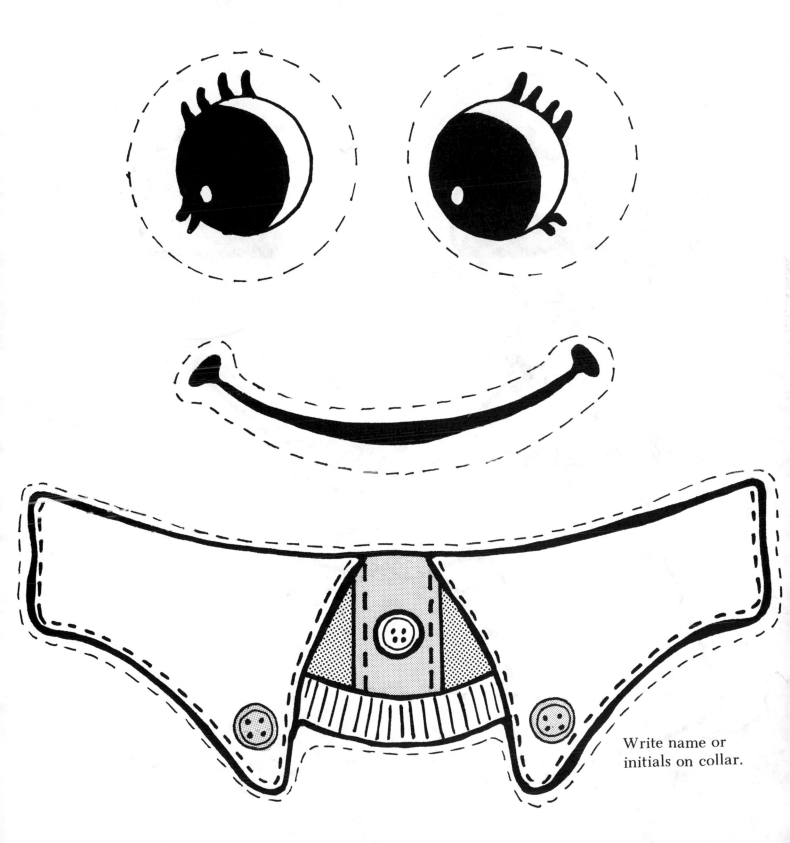

Write name or
initials on collar.

Basic Girl Pattern

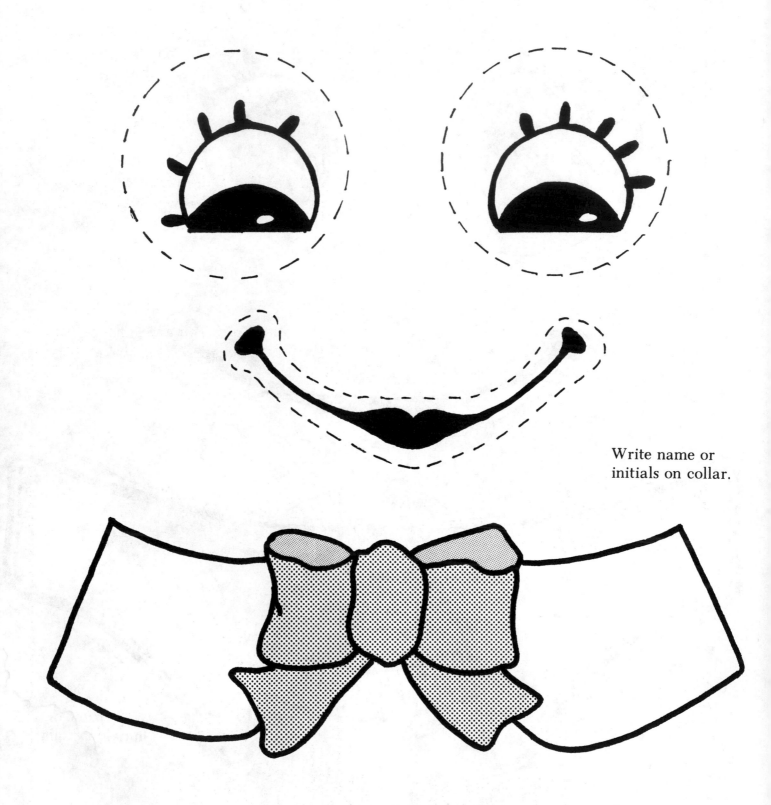

Write name or
initials on collar.

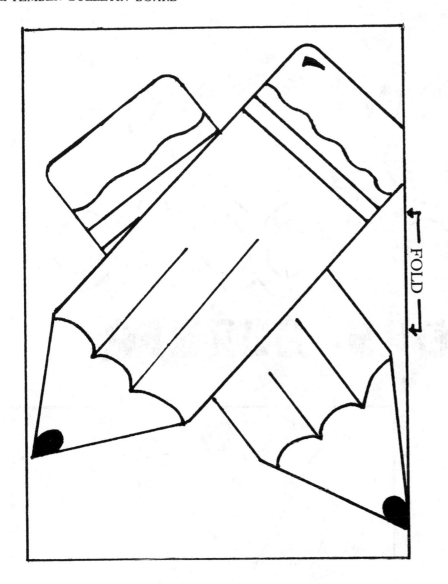

FOLD

Add a creative touch to that September bulletin board.

Follow directions below.

Measure the bulletin board surface you wish to cover. Cut as many strips as you will need. Fold strips in half and then in half again.

Trace the pencil or make a copy as shown. Place the pattern on your folded paper. Trace around it. Now cut it out except where the pencils lie on fold. You will have four pencils when you unfold the paper. You may want to use the border at the top and bottom only to make your bulletin board attractive!

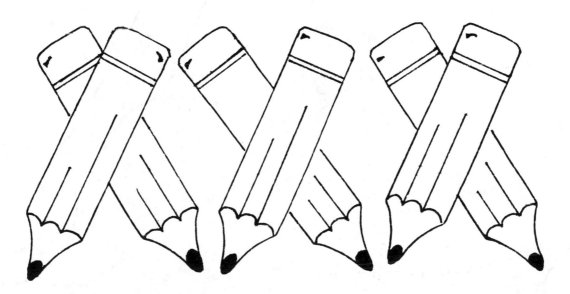

PENCIL BORDER

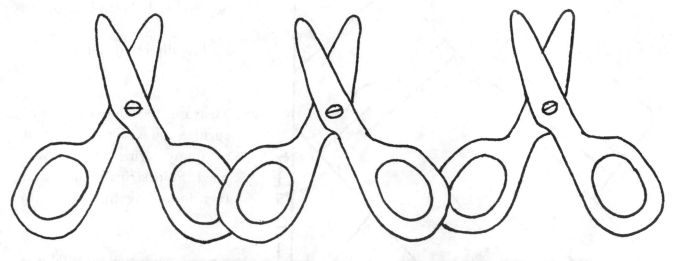

SCISSORS BORDER

Your September bulletin board will look "CLASS"Y with this decorative new border.

For easy directions, see page 9.

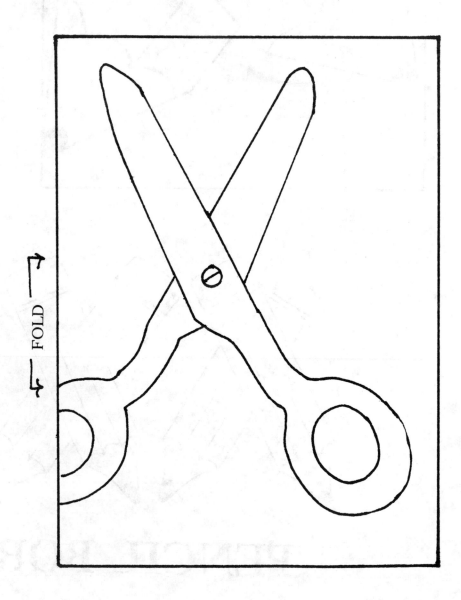

FOLD

Pur-r-fect Penmanship

SEPTEMBER

School is starting once again,
It's time to see my friends,
To share my fun-filled memories
At the summer's end.
The first day there I'm nervous,
For everything is new--
My school, my friends, and teachers,
And all my classes, too!
I hope to try my hardest
To make good grades, you see,
For my folks and all my teachers
I'll make something out of me!

WORD WIZARD

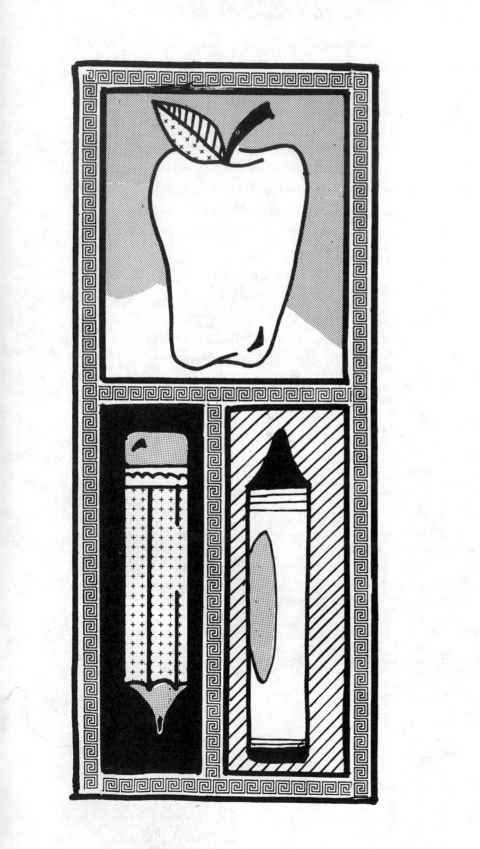

1. lunch box
2. crayons
3. September
4. glue
5. cafeteria
6. notebook
7. music
8. school
9. bus
10. art
11. principal
12. pencil
13. physical education
14. teacher
15. ruler
16. media
17. gymnasium
18. scissors
19. mathematics
20. schedule
21. eraser
22. spelling
23. penmanship
24. language
25. reading
26. flag
27. custodian
28. cook
29. patrol boy
30. fire drill
31. social studies
32. playground
33. chalkboard
34. semester

Back-to-School Bingo is a good way to welcome

students. Give each child a copy of Word Wizard or write the words on the board. The child will write any 25 words or draw pictures of them on his Bingo card. Use directions for regular Bingo when playing.

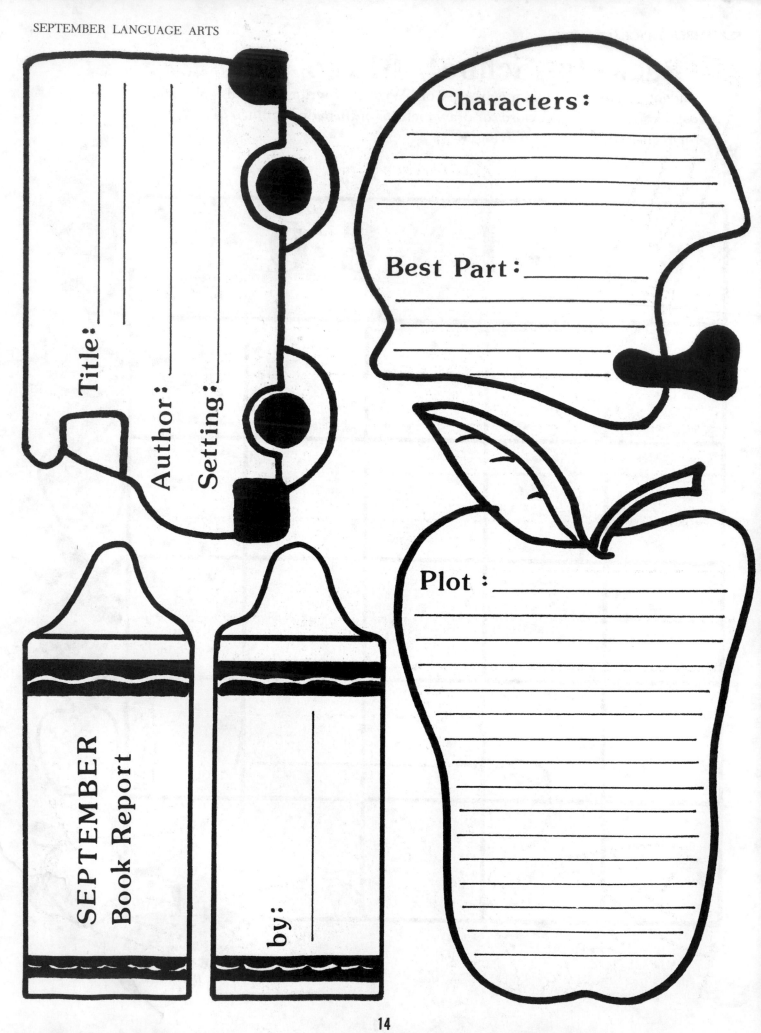

Title: _____
Author: _____
Setting: _____

Characters: _____
_____
_____
_____

Best Part: _____
_____
_____
_____

Plot: _____
_____
_____
_____
_____
_____
_____
_____
_____
_____

SEPTEMBER
Book Report

by: _____

Date

Cover-Ups

FOLLOW THESE EASY STEPS TO CREATE A COVER FOR ONE OF YOUR BOOKS!

1. Get a large brown paper grocery bag.

2. Cut down one side of a crease until you get to the bottom; then cut along bottom creases so that the bottom of the bag is completely off.

3. Smooth the paper bag and cut off any rough edges.

4. Lay the bag sideways on your desk and place your closed book in the center.

5. Draw a line across the paper at the top and bottom of your book.

6. Remove your book and fold down the top of the paper along the pencil line; then fold up the bottom section. Crease these folds well.

7. Open your book and center it on the paper.

8. Fold the left side of the paper over the left edge of the book and crease it to form a pocket.

9. Slide the left end of the book inside the pocket.

10. Fit the cover snuggly over the left half of the book; repeat crease on right side, form pocket, and slide book inside.

11. Write the book title and your name on the book cover you just completed.

12. Decorate and color your book cover.

Cover-Ups

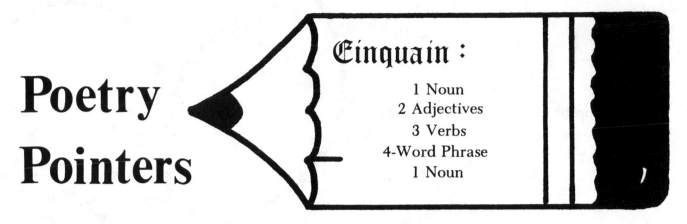

Poetry Pointers

Cinquain :

1 Noun
2 Adjectives
3 Verbs
4-Word Phrase
1 Noun

Read the cinquains written below. Study the format for writing this style of poetry. Then try to write a few cinquains of your own!

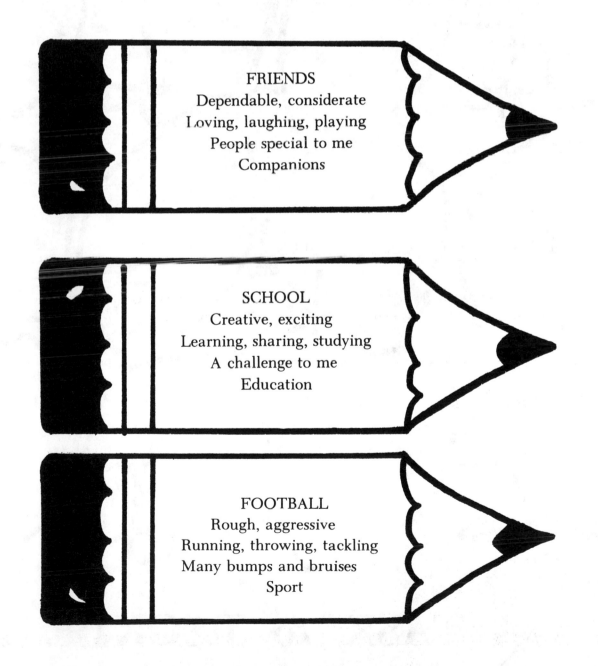

FRIENDS
Dependable, considerate
Loving, laughing, playing
People special to me
Companions

SCHOOL
Creative, exciting
Learning, sharing, studying
A challenge to me
Education

FOOTBALL
Rough, aggressive
Running, throwing, tackling
Many bumps and bruises
Sport

_____
Name

Answer all problems carefully. Color all
those you answer correctly.

A TASK to TACKLE

TOUCHDOWNS scored by players

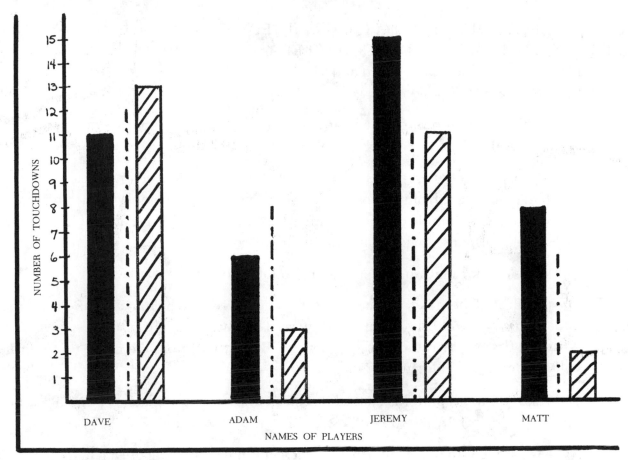

1. How many years are shown on the graph? _____
2. Which player scored the most touchdowns in all? _____
   How many? _____
3. Who scored the most touchdowns in 1981? _____
   1982? _____ 1983? _____
4. Which player's touchdowns decreased from 1981-1983? _____
5. During which two years did Jeremy's touchdowns remain the same? _____
6. Which two players scored the most touchdowns: Dave and Matt or Jeremy and Adam? _____
   _____ How many more? _____
7. In 1982, how many touchdowns were scored in all? _____
8. During what year were the most touchdowns scored? _____
9. How many more touchdowns were scored in 1982 then in 1983? _____
10. What was the total number of touchdowns scored by all players during the three years? _____

GOT A MINUTE?

HERE ARE SOME FIRST DAY, FUN-FILLED ACTIVITIES YOU MAY WANT TO TRY WITH YOUR STUDENTS TO KEEP YOUR DAY RUNNING SMOOTHLY.

1. Print YOUR name on the board and let students write as many words as they can from the letters in your name.

2. List all the bus numbers on the board vertically as children write them on paper. See who can be the first to correctly total the numbers.

3. Divide the class into two teams for this relay. Place a bell in a central location with all children equidistant from it. You name a state and the first member of each team races to the bell to ring it and correctly identify the state's capital. Give a point for each first and correct response. The team with the high score wins.

4. Try some mental math using operations suitable to your grade level.

5. Have each student make a name card for his desk. Give each child a small piece of stiff paper which he will fold in half lengthwise. Then with crayons or markers ask him to write his first name rather large in cursive. Repeat outlining the name using various colors to create a colorful design.

6. Write several math patterns on the board for children to complete on paper. Examples might include: a) 25, 30, 35, 40, ...; b) 12, 24, 36, 48, ...; c) 1, 2, 4, 7, 11, 16, ...

7. Ask each student to select a partner for these minute relays. Choose a category, such as Presidents and give the class one minute to write down as many as they can. The partners may whisper, so allow for some noise. Check answers for winning team, change categories, and repeat play. Possible category selections might include animals, flowers, trees, colors, verbs, compound words, video games, rock groups, candy bars, football teams, rivers.

8. Choose a student to stand before the class to be observed for 30 seconds. Then send him from the room. Have the children record as many details as possible about the child on a piece of paper. The winner will be the student with the most accurate answers. He will then be observed.

9. Print the alphabet across the board. Under each letter, write a number beginning with A = 1, B = 2, etc. Ask each child to print his full name vertically on his paper. Beside each letter, have him write the corresponding number. Add all the numbers to see which student's name has the greatest value.

10. Place several school items on a tray. Walk slowly once around the room as children study objects. Cover the tray and give students 1 minute to list all items they recall.

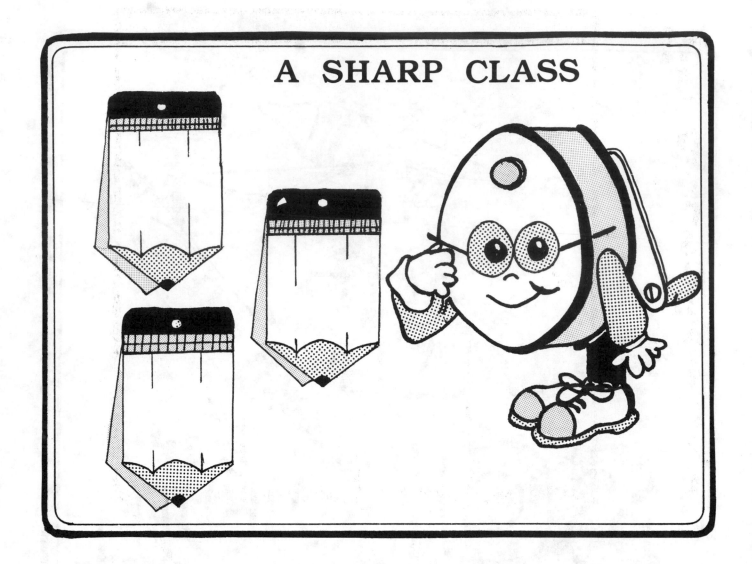

A SHARP CLASS

YOU WILL NEED:

1. Turquoise background
2. Black letters for title
3. Large cartoon-like pencil sharpener (could use movable eyes for 3-D effect)
4. Oaktag or construction paper (yellow and black) for pencils (pages 23-24)

DIRECTIONS:

Use black/yellow oaktag to make each child a copy of the Personalized Pencils found on pages 23-24. Let children complete the activity following the directions found on those pages. Add finished pencils to the bulletin board. This will not only make a nice display, but can provide a personal inventory for the teacher.

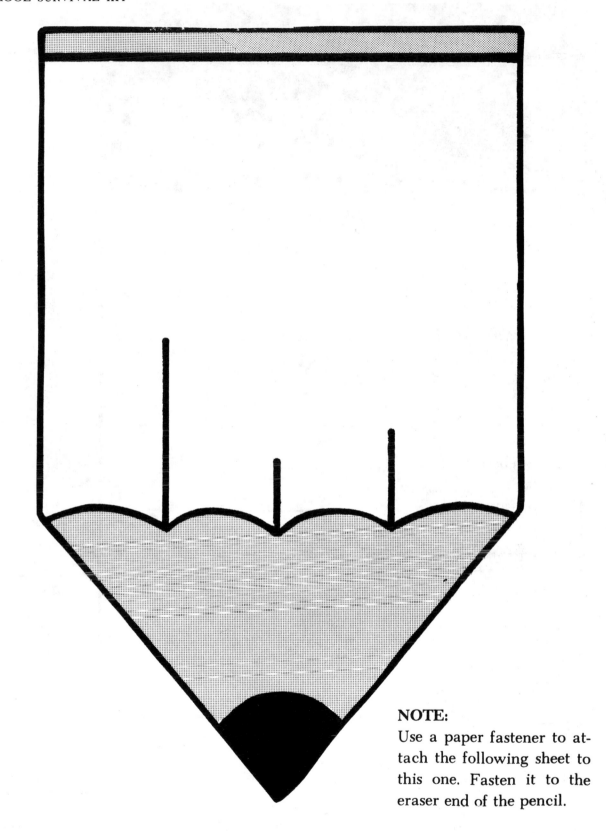

My Personalized Pencil

NOTE:
Use a paper fastener to attach the following sheet to this one. Fasten it to the eraser end of the pencil.

DIRECTIONS:
Give each child a copy of this sheet and the following page. Cut both pencils out. Ask child to print his name on the pencil to "personalize" it. (School pictures could be added.) Complete the personal information sheet on the next page before it is attached to this one. Display pencils on bulletin board.

My Personalized Pencil

My full name: _____

My nickname: _____

I was born on _____

I have _____ brothers and _____ sisters.

My favorite color is _____

I have a best friend named _____

My pets are_____

_____

In my spare time I like to _____

_____

_____

A person I admire the most is

_____

_____

is a favorite TV show of mine.

NAME

NAME TAGS

NAME

NAME

BOOKMARKS

COLOR YOURSELF A
BRIGHT SCHOOL YEAR!

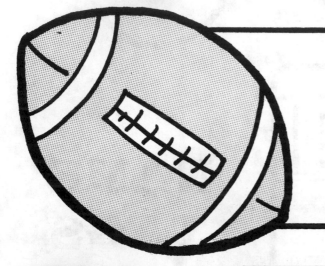

TACKLE YOUR HOMEWORK!

A GOOD BOOK GETS RIGHT TO
THE POINT

MY FRIENDS MAKE ME ONE OF THE BUNCH

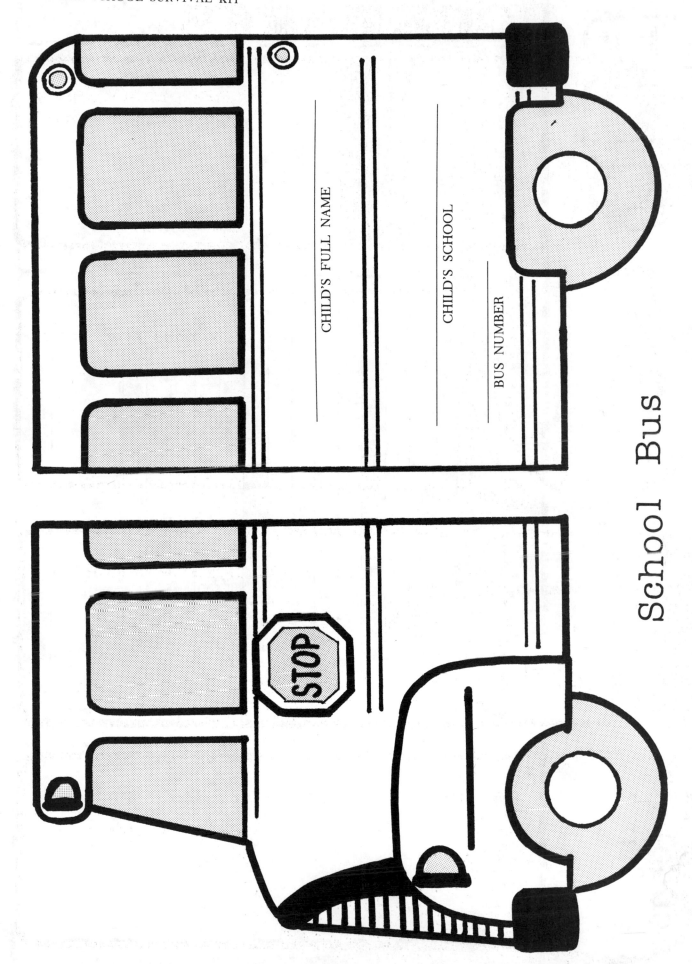

CHILD'S FULL NAME

CHILD'S SCHOOL

BUS NUMBER

STOP

School Bus

School Bus Story

DIRECTIONS:

1. Cut out body of bus.
2. Cut out story sheet and fold on dotted lines.
3. Glue bus to story sheet.
4. Write story.

PASTE BACK OF BUS HERE

fold out

fold in

BY:

fold in

fold out

PASTE FRONT OF BUS HERE

28

Fact Pack

Glue crayon box to small envelope. Cut out crayons (page 30). Write a math fact on each crayon and the answer on the back. Slide finished crayons into envelope.

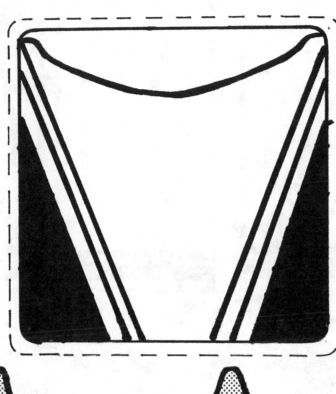

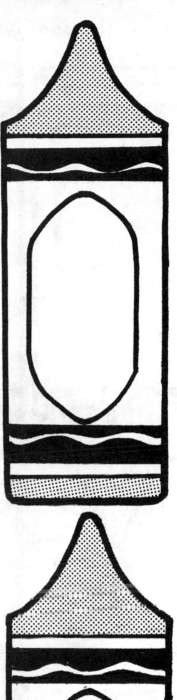

29

As A Rule, How Do You MEASURE UP?

DIRECTIONS:

Carefully cut out the ruler. Then use it to measure the objects mentioned below.

1. My desk is _____ inches long and _____ inches wide.

CUT HERE

2. The length of my right shoe is _____ inches.

3. My pencil is _____ inches long.

4. This paper is _____ inches wide.

5. It is _____ inches around my wrist.

6. My nose is about _____ inches long.

7. From top to bottom, my ear measures _____ inches.

8. My pointer finger is about _____ inches long.

9. My face from hair to chin (go over nose) measures _____ inches.

10. A person who sits near me has an ankle that is _____ inches around.

11. My math book is _____ inches long and _____ inches wide.

1
2
3
4
5
6

Don't Get "STUCK" on Your SPELLING

Write your spelling words for the week on the lines below.

1. _____
2. _____
3. _____
4. _____
5. _____
6. _____
7. _____
8. _____
9. _____
10. _____
11. _____
12. _____
13. _____
14. _____
15. _____
16. _____
17. _____
18. _____
19. _____
20. _____
21. _____
22. _____
23. _____
24. _____
25. _____

On the back of this paper write a story using as many of these words as you can!

SCHOOL GLUE

To learn these words
You must study your best
So when Friday comes
You'll pass your test!

Suggestions:
1. Write story ideas on pencils and use as a learning center.
2. Write various letters on the backs of pencils as brief penmanship lessons.

Suggestions:
1. Have children research various types of apples and where they are grown.
2. Plan an Apple Festival to exchange recipes of different apple dishes. Write recipes on apples to make booklet.

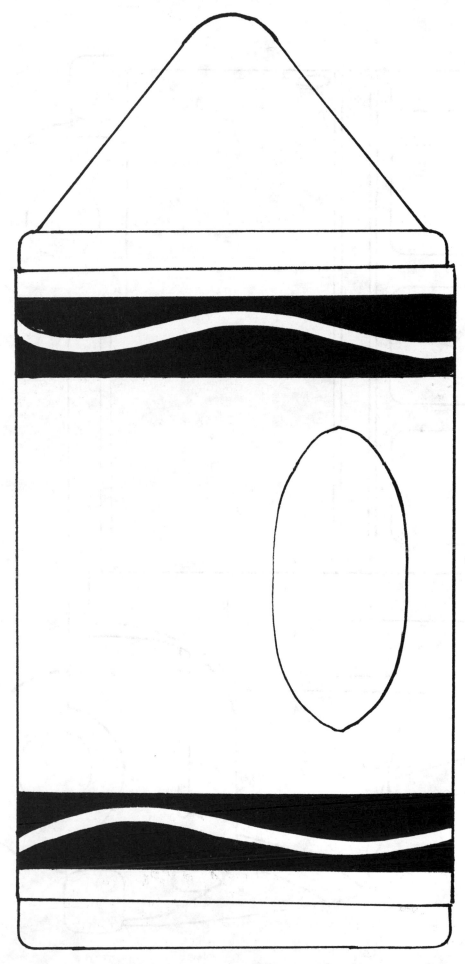

Suggestions:
1. Make a color wheel using crayons made from this pattern in a display for your room.
2. Use this page as a ditto. Have each student write his favorite color in the oval on the crayon and draw lines on the lower section so child can explain why he likes that color. Have him color the crayon.

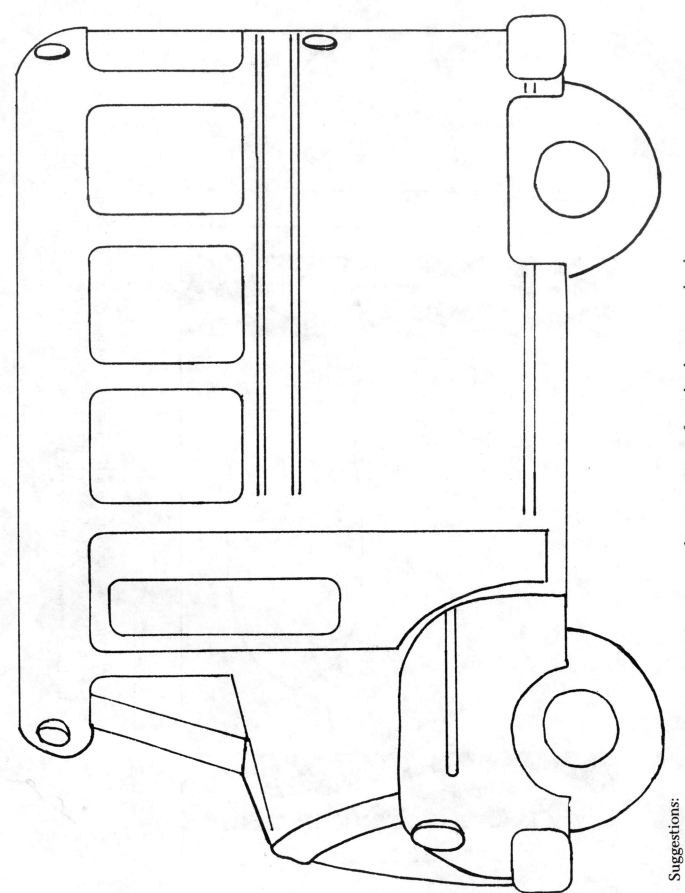

Suggestions:
1. Draw lines on the bus so child can write directions to get from his house to school.
2. Make a large bus for the classroom and display bus safety rules on it for quick reference.

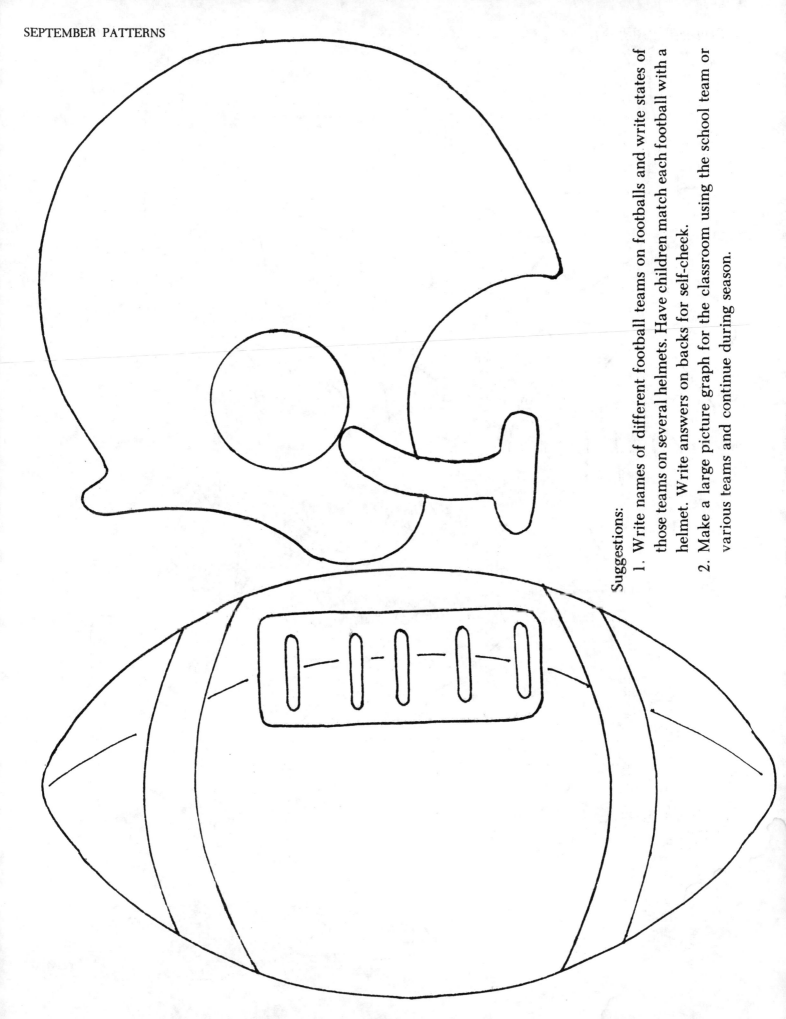

Suggestions:

1. Write names of different football teams on footballs and write states of those teams on several helmets. Have children match each football with a helmet. Write answers on backs for self-check.

2. Make a large picture graph for the classroom using the school team or various teams and continue during season.

Suggestions:
1. Ask children to make leaf collections.
2. Write names of various types of leaves phonetical-ly for children to list correctly on paper. Be sure leaves are numbered.

Teacher Tips

OCTOBER (page 39)
* Use as a coloring sheet.
* Use as a cover for an October booklet of work sheets or projects.

CALENDAR (page 42)
* Add numbers for dates, **Calendar Creations** information (page 43), and/or pictures in appropriate boxes.
* List birthdays of classmates.
* Use as a monthly weather guide.
* Assign research for gifted children to create their own calendar events.

CALENDAR CREATIONS (page 43)
* Allow students to research topics and report findings to class.
* Announce events in opening exercises each day.

GHOST TOWN (pages 44-46)
* Make this bulletin board to display **Eerie Epitaphs** (page 58) poetry after that concept is taught. Have children write their completed epitaphs on the **Tombstone Pattern** which is provided.
* For a variation of the above bulletin board, omit the small tombstones and use the **Ghost Border** on page 46 in conjunction with the **Ghost Story** creative writing sheet on page 52 and display writing papers.

PUR-R-FECT PENMANSHIP (page 49)
* Read and review the poem orally with the class, discussing format, rhyme, capital letters, and punctuation before assigning children to copy the poem in their best writing.

WORD WIZARD (page 50)
* Use the words as a spelling list for the month.
* Assign the topics for research projects.
* Use the list as a resource sheet for writing October ghost stories.

PUZZLE/GHOST STORY (pages 51-52)
* Give each child a copy of **Ghost Puzzle** with the phrases on it. Have students combine the phrases with their own thoughts to create a ghost story, which is to be written on **A "Puzzling" Ghost Story** sheet. As phrases are included in the story, that part of the puzzle should be colored. After stories are finished, children will have a puzzle to cut apart and assemble for fun as work is completed.

A HALLOWEEN SCENE (pages 53-55)
* Distribute copies of the poem, the puzzle, and **Do You Remember** as a complete language arts activity. Read and discuss the poem orally with the class, stressing the underlined vocabulary words which will be used in the puzzle. Assign the work sheet on page 55 to be finished by students independently.

LETTER OUTLINE (page 57)
* Give children this form to write home about their progress.
    > Dear Mom and Dad,
    >> Here is my work for the month of October.
    > Please look at it so you will see how I
    > am progressing . . . .

40

BEWITCHIN' MATH (page 59)

* Review the code with the class before assigning the work sheet. Let fast workers create a few of their own math problems to present on the board for others to solve. Try using this code with other math operations.

GHOST WHEEL (pages 60-61)

* Provide each student with a paper fastener to complete this activity.

CRUISIN' WITH COLUMBUS (pages 63-64)

* Divide the class so that each child has a partner. Provide each team with a gameboard and game cards so that play can begin (no prior teaching or review is necessary since information about Columbus is presented on the cards).

CHART CHALLENGE (pages 65-66)

* Use this activity to teach the concept of coordinates in plotting charts or graphs or map reading. This challenge could be used with the Columbus game or as a station with the game.

CANDY CORN FUN (page 67)

* Use the activities given here as part of a Halloween party program or a special mini activity presented earlier in the month.

SPOOKTACULAR CLUB (pages 68-71)

* Give each child a copy of the club work sheets. There is room on the pages for seven activities to be completed, so if a student wishes to create other projects, he can use the back of a work sheet or attach other papers to those provided. As activities are completed, the student should circle the number corresponding to that activity on the initiation sheet.

MINI UNIT---SPOOK SPECIALS (Ghosts)

This could be prepared as an all-day unit for intermediate or primary children. Choose work sheets in this monthly packet to include all content areas. Use the **Spook Specials**, page 72, as a cover sheet and page 73 as a checklist for you, the teacher, which shows how many activities have been completed. After you select those projects suitable to your grade level, give each project a number. For example, **Bewitchin' Math** could be project number 1, **Ghost Story** number 2, etc. Our suggestions for this mini unit could include:

1. **Ghost Puzzle** and story sheet for creative writing
2. **Bewitchin' Math** code
3. **Spooktacular Club** for art and creative thinking
4. **Ghost Town** bulletin board and **Eerie Eitaph** poetry sheet with writing on tombstones
5. **Word Wizard** list for pantomimes or creative dramatics
6. **A Halloween Scene** for language arts

Although these are merely suggestions, please adapt this unit to your individual classroom. Feel free to substitute your own ideas and projects. Some teacher preparation will be necessary for an all-day unit.

OCTOBER

Calendar Creations

OCTOBER:

2	Mahatma Gandhi's birthday
4	Frederick Remington's birthday
6	First "talking" film made debut (**The Jazz Singer**)
8	Great Fire of Chicago began
9	Leif Ericson Day
11	Eleanor Roosevelt's birthday
13	U.S. Navy began
14	William Penn's birthday
16	Oscar Wilde's birthday / Noah Webster's birthday
21	Alfred Nobel's birthday
23	Sarah Bernhardt's birthday
24	United Nations Day
25	Pablo Picasso's birthday
27	Dylan Thomas' birthday / Theodore Roosevelt's birthday
28	Jonas Salk's birthday
29	John Keats' birthday
31	National Magic Day / Halloween

GHOST TOWN

YOU WILL NEED:

1. Light blue or turquoise blue background
2. Black letters for title
3. Large white ghost
4. Brown or tan tombstones with black lettering and details (page 45 for pattern)

DIRECTIONS:

Give each student a tombstone. Use **Eerie Epitaph** poetry sheet (page 58) as the basis for this lesson. Display finished writing by attaching tombstones to the bulletin board.

TOMBSTONE PATTERN

GHOST BORDER

Try this to brighten that October bulletin board. For directions, see page 9.

fold

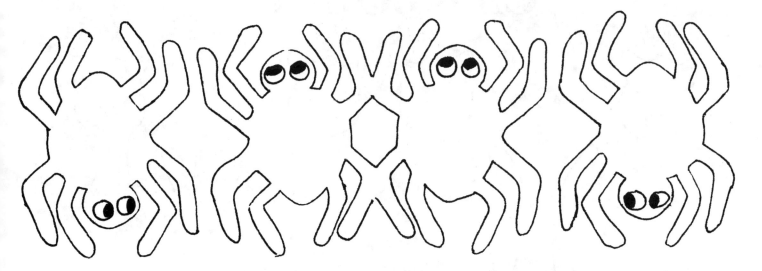

SPIDER BORDER

These creepy, crawly creatures are certain to attract eyes to your fall or science bulletin board.

For directions to complete this spider border, see page 9.

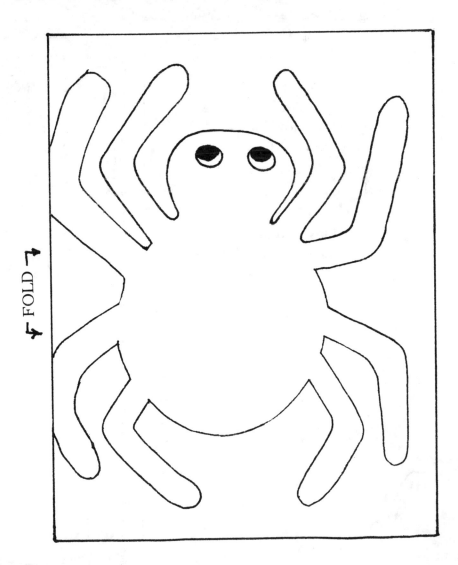

FOLD

CAT BORDER

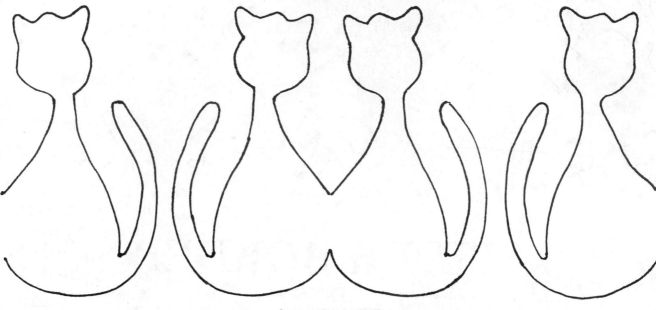

Introduce these lovable cats to your children on that October bulletin board.

For directions to make this cat border, see page 9.

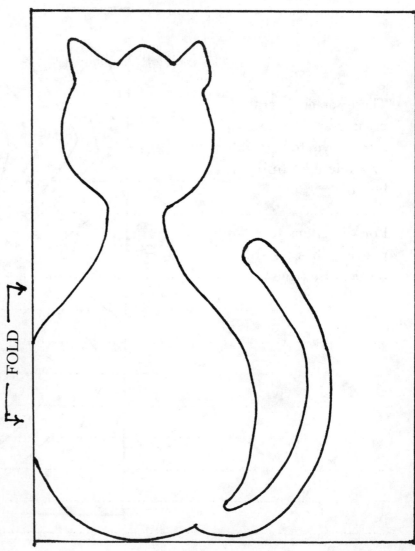

FOLD

48

Purr-r-fect Penmanship

OCTOBER

The sky is blue,
The days are warm,
The sun shines overhead;
The nights are cool,
The air is crisp
When I crawl into bed.
The leaves once green,
Are red and orange,
And some, a brown or gold.
Autumn is here.
Oh! What a sight
For my eyes to behold!

WORD WIZARD

1. October
2. Halloween
3. cat
4. witch
5. moon
6. bat
7. costume
8. mask
9. broomstick
10. spider
11. graveyard
12. web
13. Columbus Day
14. hunting
15. party
16. jack-o'-lantern
17. candy
18. football
19. ghost
20. scary
21. leaves
22. trick or treat
23. masquerade
24. scarecrow
25. goblin
26. squirrel
27. nuts
28. skeleton
29. haunted house
30. spook

GHOST PUZZLE

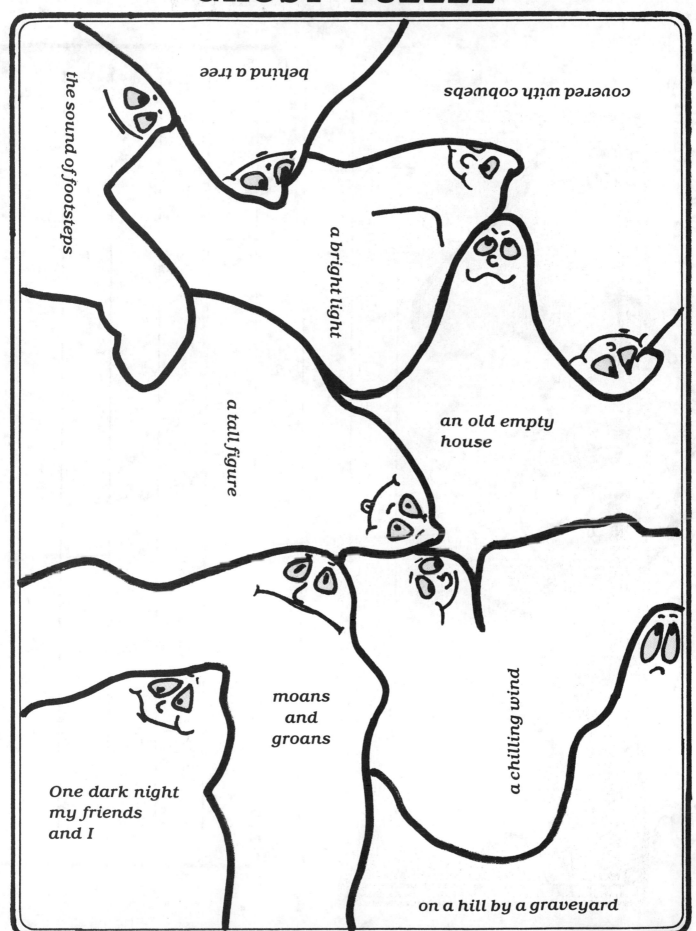

behind a tree

covered with cobwebs

the sound of footsteps

a bright light

a tall figure

an old empty house

moans and groans

a chilling wind

One dark night my friends and I

on a hill by a graveyard

A "Puzzling" Ghost Story

FOLD IN

FOLD IN

A HALLOWEEN SCENE

There is a creepy, old **haunted** house
On top of a high, **windy** hill.
It has broken windows and crooked **doors**
And **spiders** on every **sill**.

The cob**webs dangle** when blown by the wind,
Field mice **scurry** in and out;
Floors do creak and the **stairs** will squeak
When the ghost begins moving about.

Now this sneaky old lady who lives in the house
Goes to town one day every year.
She fills a sack placed on her back
And as the evening nears,

She winds her way back up the hill,
Her long nose just a **twitchin'**--
You never know what's on her mind
As she enters the **ghouly** old kitchen.

A big, black **cauldron** is on the stove,
Before too long, it's full
Of spiders' legs, bat wings and cats,
And blood to soften the **skull**.

Soon the **brew** begins to boil,
It turns **crimson** and thickens.
And all throughout that haunted house
The **odor** begins to sicken.

It makes the creepy, **haggardy** lady
Run quickly from the room.
She **seeks** her cat and **frazzled** black hat,
And rides away on her broom.

The moon is **crested** in the sky,
Her **silhouette** makes a scene.
Silently she glides about--
She'll return again next **Halloween**!

A HALLOWEEN SCENE

ACROSS:

1 October 31 holiday
3 Noise a ghost makes
7 Head covering
10 Smell
12 Jerkin'
13 Worn-out
15 Breezy
16 Looks for
18 Peaked
19 Window ledge
21 Fray
22 What a witch cooks in
23 Hag

DOWN:

1 Spooked
2 Entrance into a house
4 Ghostly
5 Steps
6 Deep red
8 Hurry
9 Outline or profile
11 Hang freely
14 Bones of the head
15 What a spider spins
17 Eight-legged creatures
20 Witch's drink

NOTE: You will find all but one of these answers in the
poem!

A Halloween Scene

Draw a scene from the poem in the space below. Color it.

DO YOU REMEMBER?

Answer these questions without looking back in the poem.

1. What is found on every windowsill?

2. How often does the witch go to town?

3. When does she return home?

4. Where does the witch carry her sack?

5. What part of her body twitches?

6. What cooks in the cauldron?

7. What color is the brew?

8. Why does the witch leave the room?

9. What two things does the witch seek?

10. When will the witch return?

Title:_____
_____
Author:_____
Setting:_____
Characters :_____
_____
_____
_____
_____

Best Part :
_____
_____
_____
_____
_____
_____

OCTOBER
Book Report

by:_____
_____

Plot:_____
_____
_____
_____
_____
_____
_____
_____
_____
_____

Date

_____ ,

_____

_____

_____

_____

_____

_____

_____

_____ ,

_____

EERIE EPITAPHS

An **EPITAPH** is an inscription on a tombstone in memory of someone who died.

Read these EPITAPHS and then try a few of your own.

Here lies my teacher, old Miss Blass -
I was the smartest kid in her class!

Here lies my pet, a dog named Rover.
When hit by a car, his life was over.

A baseball bat and ball used often
Are buried with Michael in his coffin.

The babysitter we drove insane
Was killed when hit with Jeremy's train.

Old Mr. Crow, the village baker,
Just got back from the undertaker.

While sitting here sleeping in a paper sack,
I got run over on the railroad track.

Here lies my friend, a gal from the South.
She died when she tried to put her foot in her mouth.

58

BEWITCHIN' MATH

1.

2.

3.

4.

5.

6.

7.

8.

GHOST WHEEL

GHOST WHEEL

Choose a math operation. Write the problem in the rectangle. Turn the wheel over and write the answer on the back. Cut out the wheel and use a paper fastener to attach it to the other half of the ghost wheel (page 60). Although this wheel was presented as a math project, it can easily be adapted to any content area.

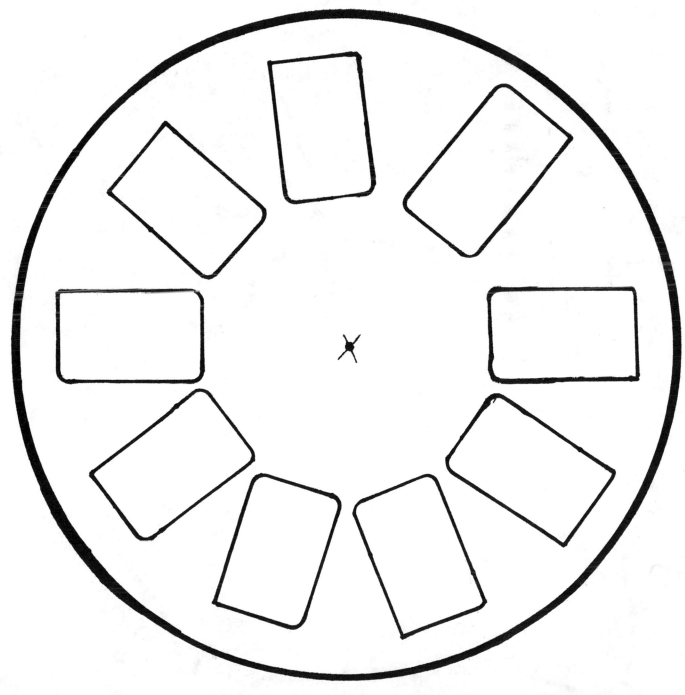

We're in the "SPIRIT" of SUBTRACTION....

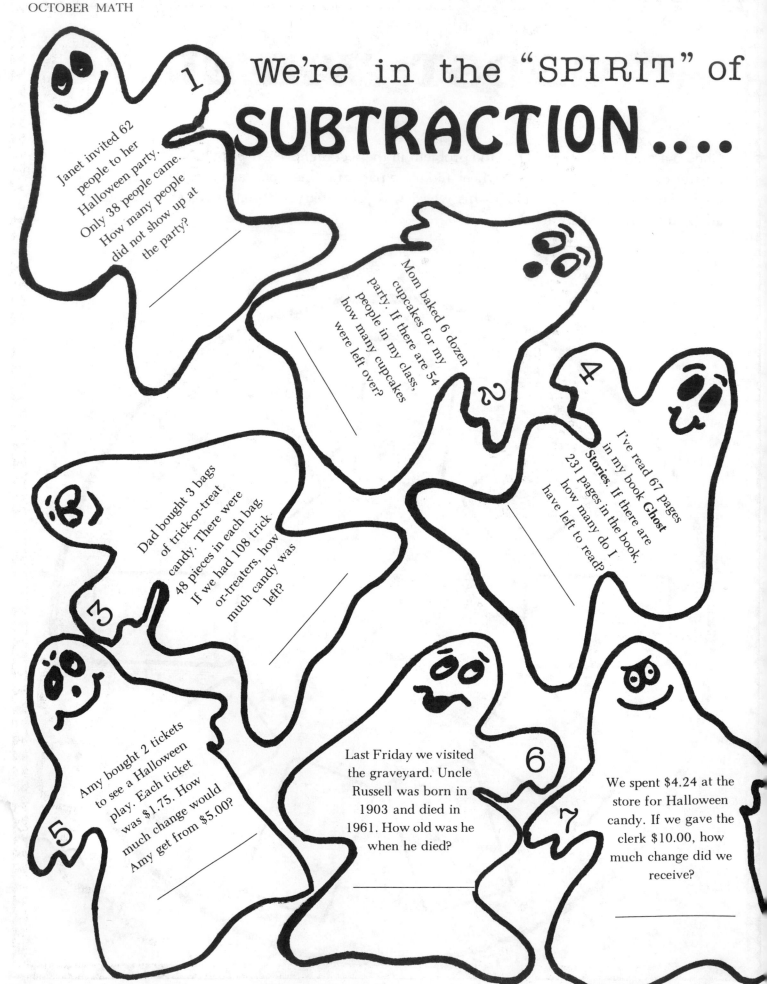

1. Janet invited 62 people to her Halloween party. Only 38 people came. How many people did not show up at the party? _____

2. Mom baked 6 dozen cupcakes for my party. If there are 54 people in my class, how many cupcakes were left over? _____

4. I've read 67 pages in my book **Ghost Stories**. If there are 231 pages in the book, how many do I have left to read? _____

3. Dad bought 3 bags of trick-or-treat candy. There were 48 pieces in each bag. If we had 108 trick-or-treaters, how much candy was left? _____

5. Amy bought 2 tickets to see a Halloween play. Each ticket was $1.75. How much change would Amy get from $5.00? _____

6. Last Friday we visited the graveyard. Uncle Russell was born in 1903 and died in 1961. How old was he when he died? _____

7. We spent $4.24 at the store for Halloween candy. If we gave the clerk $10.00, how much change did we receive? _____

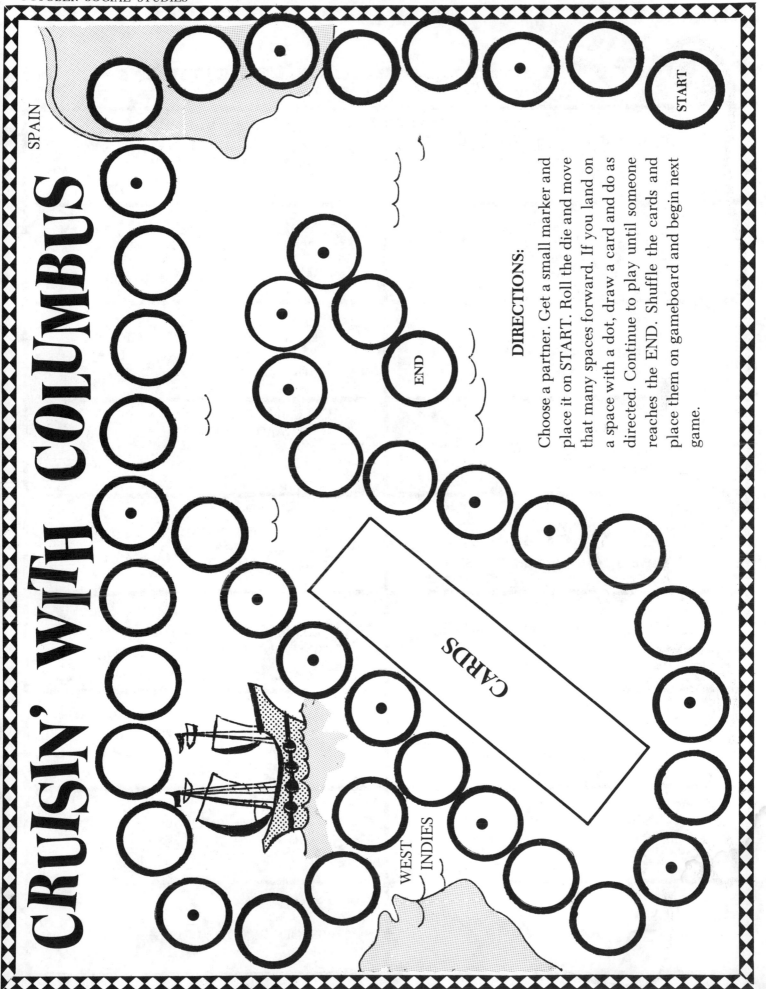

CRUISIN' WITH COLUMBUS

SPAIN

START

DIRECTIONS:

Choose a partner. Get a small marker and place it on START. Roll the die and move that many spaces forward. If you land on a space with a dot, draw a card and do as directed. Continue to play until someone reaches the END. Shuffle the cards and place them on gameboard and begin next game.

END

CARDS

WEST INDIES

Game Cards for "Cruisin' with Columbus"

CHRISTOPHER COLUMBUS BORN IN GENOA, ITALY, IN 1451. MOVE AHEAD 2 SPACES.	THE **NIÑA** AND **PINTA** ARE SEPARATED IN A STORM IN THE AZORES. GO BACK 3 SPACES.
CHRISTOPHER COLUMBUS IS THE OLDEST OF FIVE CHILDREN. MOVE AHEAD 1 SPACE.	KING FERDINAND AND QUEEN ISABELLA GIVE COLUMBUS THE TITLE "ADMIRAL OF THE OCEAN SEA." MOVE AHEAD 3 SPACES.
COLUMBUS TRIES TO FIND A SHORT SEA ROUTE TO THE INDIES. MOVE AHEAD 3 SPACES.	COLUMBUS DISCOVERS THE ISLAND OF JAMAICA. MOVE AHEAD 2 SPACES.
COLUMBUS HAD TWO SONS, DIEGO AND FERDINAND. MOVE AHEAD 2 SPACES.	COLUMBUS TAKES TEEN-AGE BOYS ON BOARD HIS FOURTH AND FINAL VOYAGE BECAUSE OF THEIR DESIRE FOR ADVENTURE AND THEIR YOUTH. MOVE AHEAD 2 SPACES.
KING FERDINAND AND QUEEN ISABELLA OF SPAIN OFFER TO HELP COLUMBUS. MOVE AHEAD 1 SPACE.	HURRICANE DESTROYS MOST OF COLUMBUS' SHIPS. MOVE BACK 3 SPACES.
COLUMBUS GETS THREE SHIPS: THE **NIÑA**, **PINTA**, AND **SANTA MARÍA**. MOVE AHEAD 1 SPACE.	COLUMBUS MAROONED ON JAMAICA FOR YEAR. GO BACK 1 SPACE.
THE SHIPS GIVEN TO COLUMBUS WERE MADE OF WOOD AND HAD NO ENGINES OR MOTORS. MOVE BACK 2 SPACES.	QUEEN ISABELLA DIES. GO BACK 2 SPACES.
COLUMBUS LANDS ON THE ISLAND OF SAN SALVADOR. MOVE AHEAD 2 SPACES.	CHRISTOPHER COLUMBUS MEETS FIGHTING INDIANS. GO BACK 1 SPACE.
THE **SANTA MARÍA** WRECKS ON A REEF. GO BACK TO START.	CHRISTOPHER COLUMBUS DIES. LOSE 1 TURN.

Chart Challenge

Use the code on the next page to solve the secret message. Write your answers on the chart below. Use all capital letters.

9										
8										
7										
6										
5										
4										
3										
2										
1										
0										
	A	**B**	**C**	**D**	**E**	**F**	**G**	**H**	**I**	**J**

Chart Challenge

Chart your course! Here's the code.

1.	E,1	write 4		25.	E,5	write H
2.	D,3	write M		26.	G,4	write E
3.	F,6	write O		27.	I,3	write A
4.	D,8	write W		28.	D,6	write P
5.	I,9	write S		29.	D,9	write L
6.	C,4	write S		30.	D,5	write W
7.	F,7	write N		31.	H,9	write U
8.	B,9	write C		32.	E,8	write A
9.	H,6	write E		33.	F,1	write 9
10.	J,4	write D		34.	I,6	write R
11.	F,8	write S		35.	E,3	write E
12.	E,9	write U		36.	D,4	write C
13.	G,1	write 2		37.	F,9	write M
14.	F,3	write R		38.	G,3	write I
15.	E,4	write O		39.	F,5	write O
16.	H,4	write R		40.	B,4	write I
17.	E,6	write L		41.	C,3	write A
18.	A,4	write D		42.	E,2	write I
19.	F,4	write V		43.	I,4	write E
20.	G,9	write B		44.	D,1	write 1
21.	E,7	write A		45.	G,6	write R
22.	F,2	write N		46.	C,9	write O
23.	H,3	write C		47.	B,6	write E
24.	C,6	write X				

HERE ARE SOME ACTIVITIES YOU MAY WISH TO TRY WITH YOUR CLASS.

1. Fill a jar with candy corn and have students estimate the number of pieces in the jar. The child guessing the exact amount wins the jar of candy corn.

2. Write the ingredients in candy corn on the board. Discuss these with the children. Have them copy the words as a penmanship lesson.

3. Develop a creative writing activity using the topics below or those of your own choice:
   a) From Factory to Mouth
   b) A Ride in a Trick-or-Treat Bag
   c) How Candy Corn Got Its Name
   d) My Candy Corn Advertisement

4. Plan relays using candy corn as the theme.
   a) Divide the class into teams. Give each team a spoon and a small container of candy corn. Have each child on the team run with a few pieces of candy corn on a spoon to the end of the room and back without spilling any. Continue the exercise until the team has finished.
   b) Place two containers at the head of each team at the opposite end of the room. Put all the candy corn in one container. Students must run down and spoon the pieces from the full container to the empty one without spilling any. The next student will then empty that container into the other one, and so on. Continue play until a team wins.
   c) Hide the candy corn in a large room, or outside if it is dry. Give students a time limit to see which team can find the most pieces of candy corn.

5. Bake cookies or cupcakes with your class and let the students decorate with the pieces of candy corn to make faces or other designs.

6. Use the shape of candy corn to introduce your students to the concept of a triangle. Then allow the students time to create an art picture using nothing but triangles.

7. Print the words CANDY CORN in large letters on the board. Give students a few minutes to write down as many words as they can using the letters found in the words. A variation of this activity would be to have students list as many words as they can think of that begin with a hard c sound.

YOU ARE INVITED TO JOIN A SPOOKTACULAR CLUB

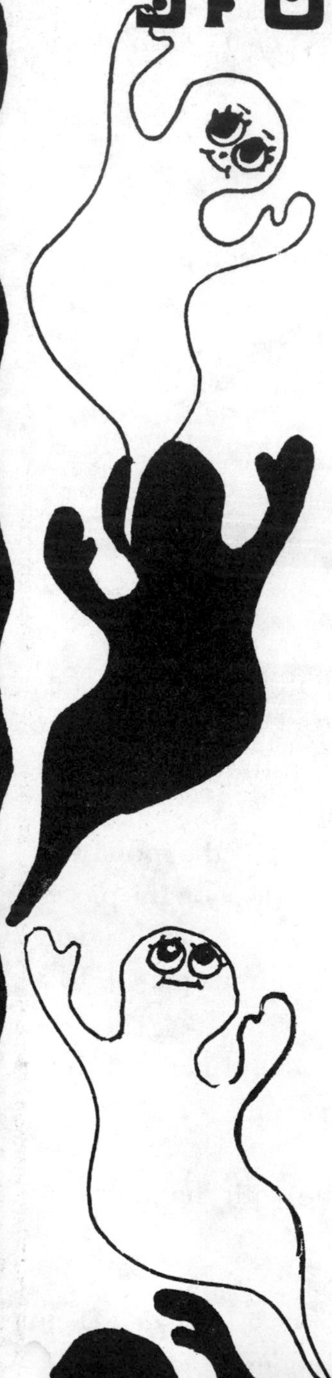

Complete these for your INITIATION:

1. Motto
2. Club Rules
3. Symbol
4. Membership Card
5. Spook Tricks
6. Club Song
7. License Plate
8. Other (secret hand-shake, drawing of clubhouse, etc.)

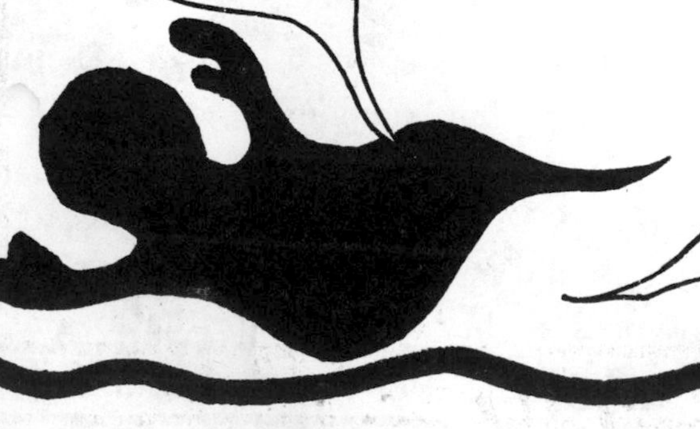

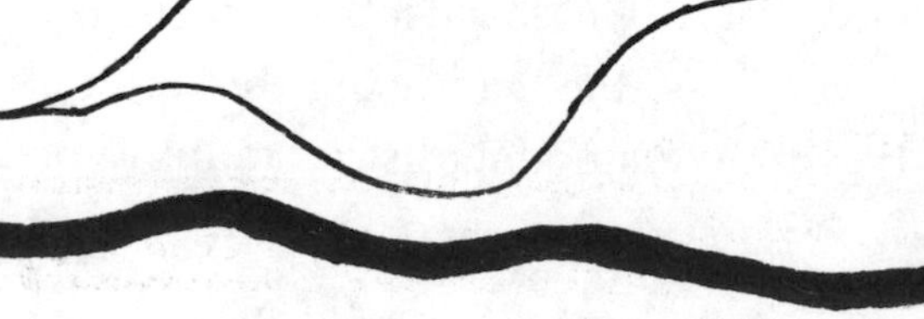

Motto:

ELUB RULES:

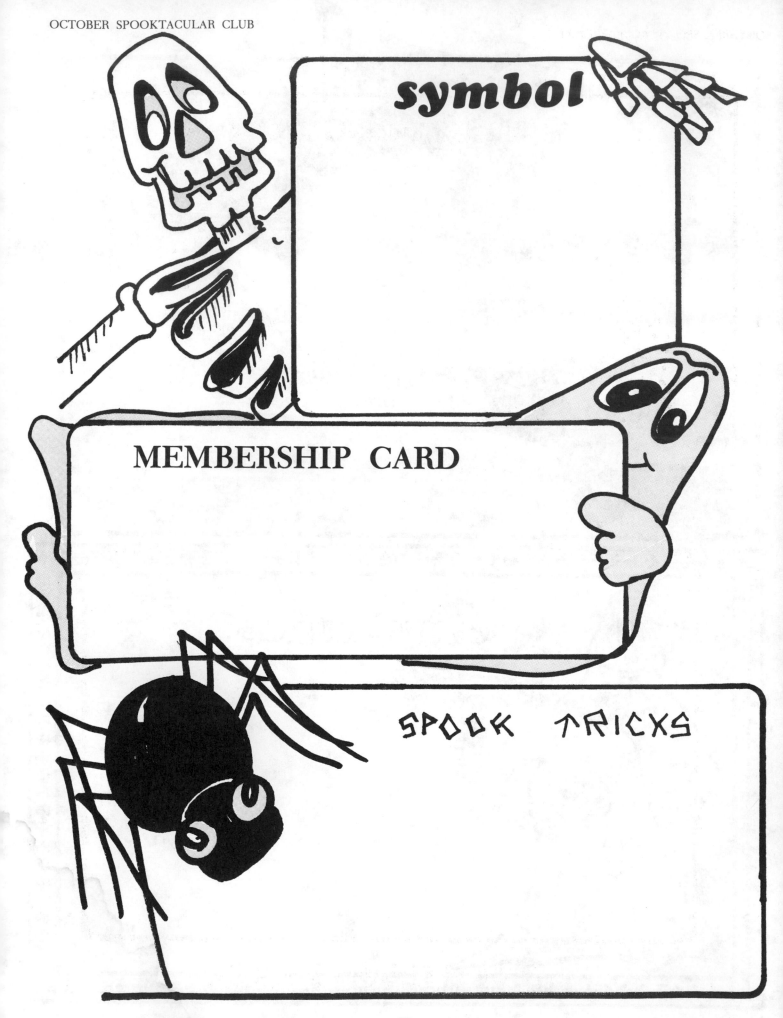

symbol

MEMBERSHIP CARD

SPOOK TRICXS

CLUB SONG

LICENSE PLATE

SPOOK SPECIALS

SPOOK SPECIALS

Color in the bat as you complete the ghost activity which corresponds with it. Keep all projects in order in your folder.

Suggestions:
1. Make a large cat to use on your "Purr"-fect Pet bulletin board. Let children write research findings on smaller cats to display on board.
2. Write **er**, **ur**, **ir**, and **or** words on cats to display in the room at a language arts center.

Suggestions:
  1. As a vocabulary study, write words on witch that describe her.
  2. Use those words from suggestion one to create a story.

Suggestions:
1. Use as a ditto for a coloring sheet or booklet cover.
2. Use on a bulletin board with vocabulary words, numbers, pictures, objects, etc., coming from top of pumpkin.

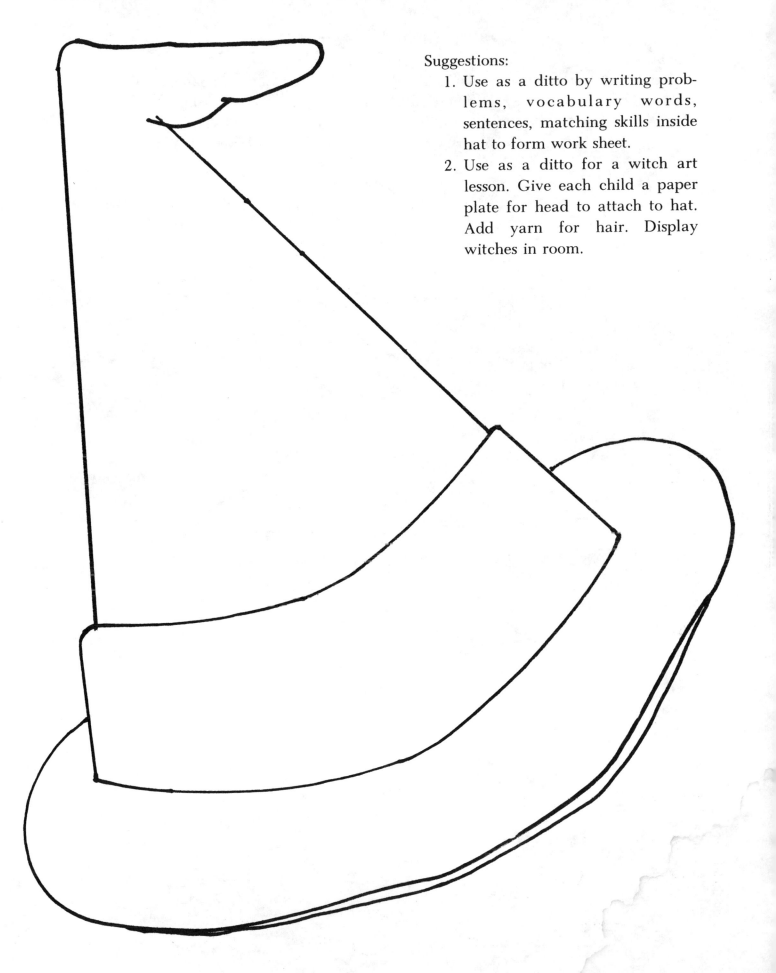

Suggestions:
1. Use as a ditto by writing problems, vocabulary words, sentences, matching skills inside hat to form work sheet.
2. Use as a ditto for a witch art lesson. Give each child a paper plate for head to attach to hat. Add yarn for hair. Display witches in room.

Suggestions:
1. Use ghost on a bulletin board entitled "Introducing Halloween Safety." On smaller ghosts write safety rules to follow when trick-or-treating.
2. Change bulletin board title to "Introducing (name a specific skill)." On little ghosts write vocabulary words, math problems, Halloween words, etc.

Suggestions:
1. Place large bat on bulletin board. Write various numbers on smaller bats to place on board. Each day change operations for solving math problems. Examples: 1) add all bats; 2) multiply all bats; 3) add the three largest numbered bats and divide by 4.
2. Place large bat on bulletin board. Scramble Halloween words to put on smaller bats and display on board. Have children unscramble words, write them 4 times each, and use them in sentences.

NOVEMBER

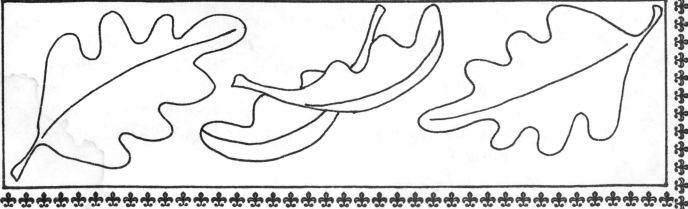

Teacher Tips

NOVEMBER (page 80)
* Use as a coloring sheet.
* Use as a cover for a November booklet of work sheets or projects.

CALENDAR (page 83)
* Add numbers for dates, **Calendar Creations** information (page 84), and/or pictures in appropriate boxes.
* List birthdays of classmates.
* Use as a monthly weather guide.
* Assign research for gifted children to create their own calendar events.

CALENDAR CREATIONS (page 84)
* Allow students to research topics and report findings to class.
* Announce events in opening exercises each day.

DRUMSTICKS ON PARADE (pages 85-87)
* Follow the directions provided for the class to complete the art lesson; older students may not need patterns.

RAVIN' GOOD WORK (pages 88-91)
* Make this bulletin board to display good papers after students complete the creative writing assignments. The small ravens on which story ideas have been written could be shown in a small bird nest on the bulletin board or displayed at the corner of each child's writing paper as it is placed on the bulletin board. Although the bulletin board was designed as a display for creative stories, any type of good work could be presented.

PUR-R-FECT PENMANSHIP (page 94)
* Read and discuss this three-verse limerick-style poem with the class, reviewing format, rhyme, capital letters, and punctuation before assigning children to copy the poem in their best writing.

WORD WIZARD (page 95)
* Use the words as a spelling list for the month.
* Assign the topics for research projects.
* Use the list as a resource sheet for writing November stories.

TRICK THE TURKEY (pages 96-97)
* Use this game to reinforce **Word Wizard** words by setting it up as a station in the room, or by providing a copy for the children to use with a partner.
* Use the gameboard provided but substitute your own spelling list to reinforce those words.

A BOASTFUL ROASTFULL (pages 98-101)
* Try this choral reading with your children. Assign various parts and read it several times. Let the class make the finger puppets (patterns on pages 100 and 101) and present a show to other children.

LETTER OUTLINE (page 103)

* Give children this form to write home about their progress.

> Dear Mom and Dad,
>
> Here is my work for the month of November.
>
> Please look at it so you will see how I
>
> am progressing . . . .

TURKEY TRIPLETS (page 104)

* Review the poetic form for triplets. Read and discuss the triplets presented and assist the children in writing some of their own.

WEIGHT GAINED BY TILLIE TURKEY (page 107)

* Review the concept of line graphs before giving this work sheet to the class for completion.

TURKEY TIME (pages 108-116)

* Distribute copies of this entire mini booklet for the children to color, cut out, staple, and complete. You will be able to supply math problems, vocabulary words, creative writing ideas, etc., on the **Hot Roll Review** page included in this section. You may also wish to have the entire class create a code together to make the **Cranberry Sauce Spelling** easier to check.

MINI UNIT--TURKEYS

This could be prepared as an all-day unit for intermediate or primary children. Choose work sheets in this packet to include all content areas. Our suggestions include:

1. **November** cover sheet for booklet of work sheets (page 80)
2. **Drumsticks on Parade** bulletin board/art project (pages 85-87)
3. **Pur-r-fect Penmanship** work sheet for handwriting (page 94)
4. **Trick the Turkey** gameboard and game cards for spelling (pages 96-97)
5. **A Boastful Roastfull** choral reading sheets and puppets patterns for a language arts/creative drama presentation (pages 98-101)
6. **Turkey Triplets** for poetry (page 104)
7. **Trim the Turkey** or **Hunting for Something?** for math (choose one appropriate for your grade level) (pages 105 or 106)
8. **Weight Gained by Tillie** for social studies (page 107)
9. **Turkey Time** booklet (if you choose to do this with your class, you may want to eliminate some or all of the above activities) (pages 108-116)

Slight preparations may be necessary as the activities are adapted to the needs of your classroom. You may wish to supplement with some of your own materials.

NOVEMBER

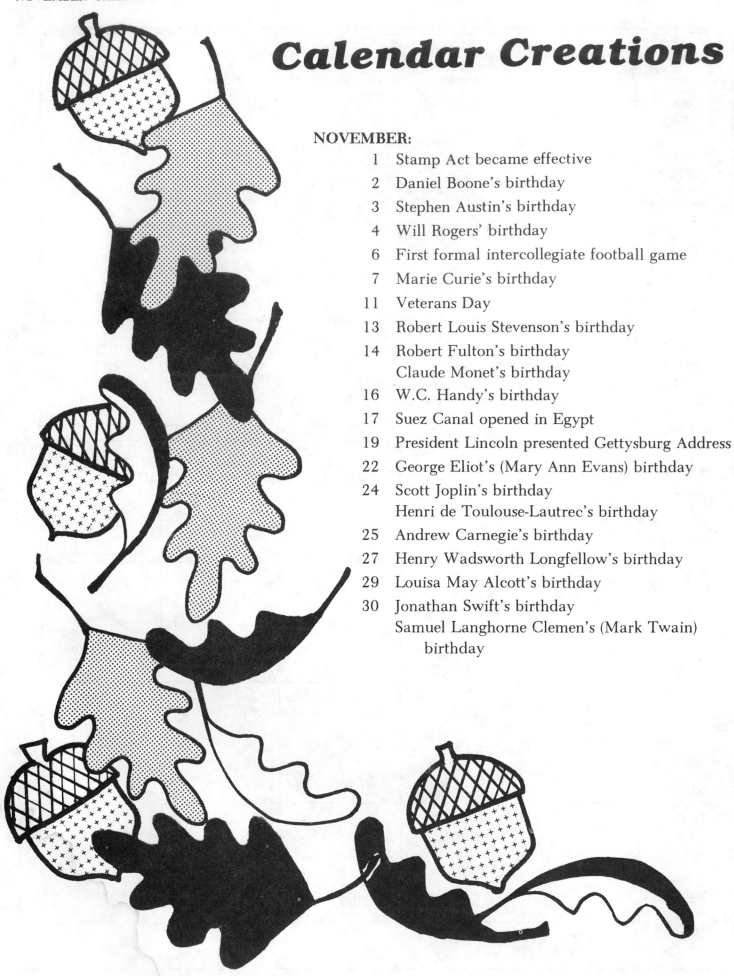

Calendar Creations

NOVEMBER:

1   Stamp Act became effective

2   Daniel Boone's birthday

3   Stephen Austin's birthday

4   Will Rogers' birthday

6   First formal intercollegiate football game

7   Marie Curie's birthday

11 Veterans Day

13 Robert Louis Stevenson's birthday

14 Robert Fulton's birthday
     Claude Monet's birthday

16 W.C. Handy's birthday

17 Suez Canal opened in Egypt

19 President Lincoln presented Gettysburg Address

22 George Eliot's (Mary Ann Evans) birthday

24 Scott Joplin's birthday
     Henri de Toulouse-Lautrec's birthday

25 Andrew Carnegie's birthday

27 Henry Wadsworth Longfellow's birthday

29 Louisa May Alcott's birthday

30 Jonathan Swift's birthday
     Samuel Langhorne Clemen's (Mark Twain)
       birthday

Drumsticks

on Parade

YOU WILL NEED:

1. Yellow background
2. Black letters for title
3. Brown paper for drumsticks (pattern on page 87)
4. Various colors of construction paper for drumstick clothing (pattern page 86)

DIRECTIONS:

Give each child a drumstick pattern and paper. Young children may need the clothing patterns, but older students may want to design their own outfits. Display finished drumsticks on the bulletin board.

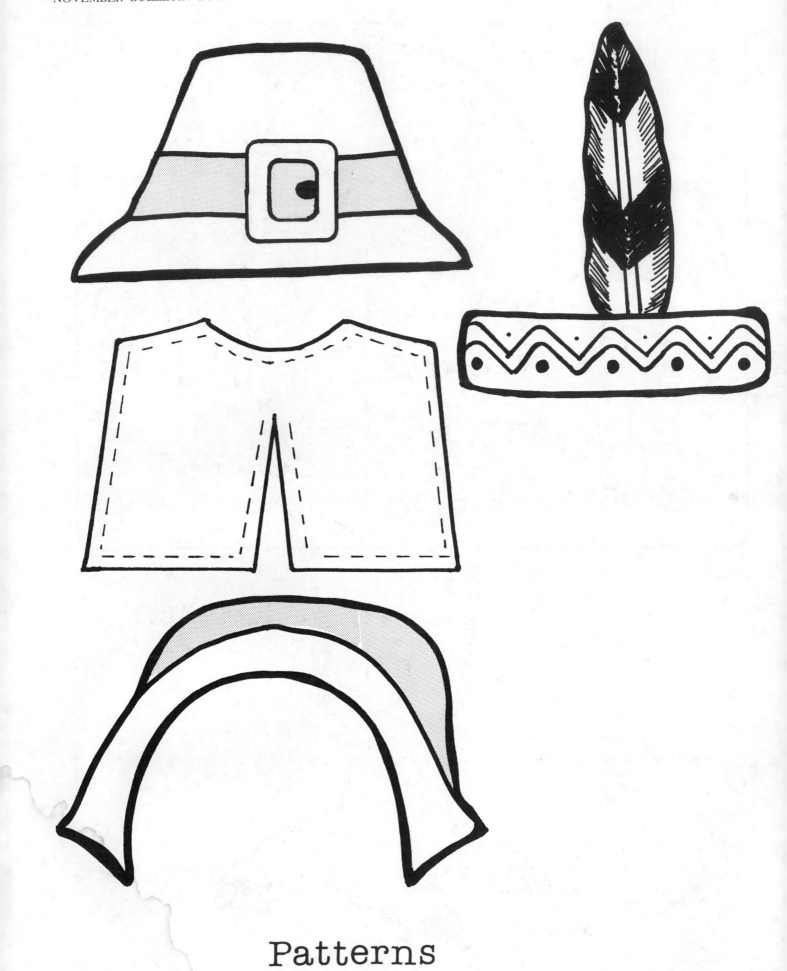

Patterns

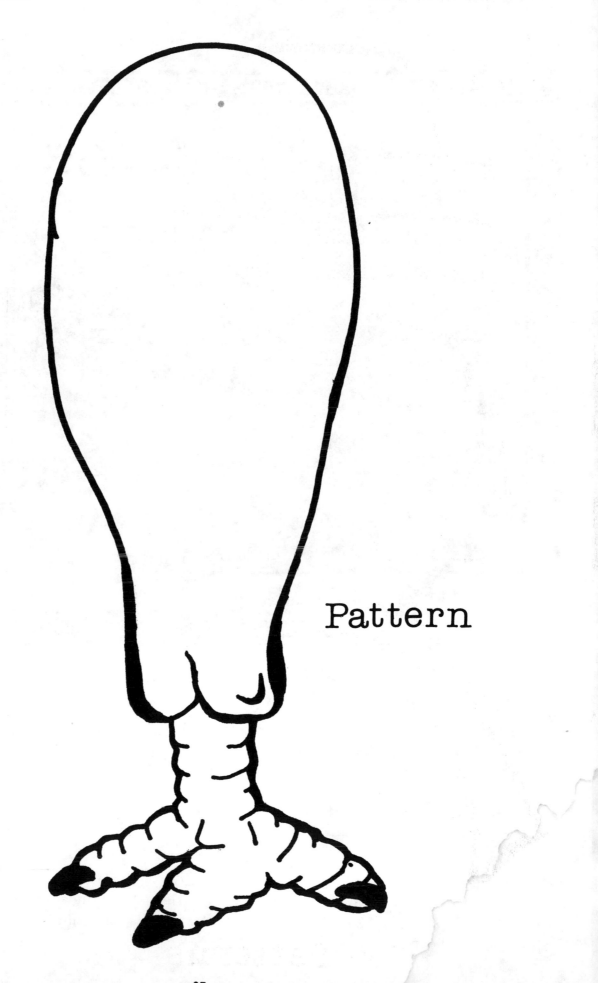

Pattern

YOU WILL NEED:

1. Yellow background
2. Black letters for title
3. One large black raven and several smaller ones (patterns on pages 89-90) to place beside writing papers
4. Large brown branch with bright leaves on which to place raven

DIRECTIONS:

Give each child a handwriting sheet. Have him write a story using one of the ideas presented on the raven or one of his own. Display finished papers on the bulletin board.

RAVEN PATTERN

Because you were born an albino, you are totally unlike all other ravens. Describe what it is like.

Pretend that a farmer has just made you his scarecrow. Describe your day.

Pretend you are an animal. Tell what animal you would be and how you prepare yourself for winter.

Compare and contrast the raven to another kind of bird.

My favorite season of the year is fall because.....

A favorite fall holiday is Thanksgiving. Write a story about the way your family celebrates this special day.

Ravin' story ideas

90

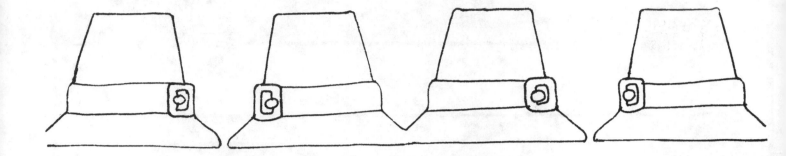

HAT BORDER

This would be the perfect border for a Thanksgiving bulletin board. It would be ideal to use with Pilgrim children patterns included in this November section.

For hat border directions, see page 9.

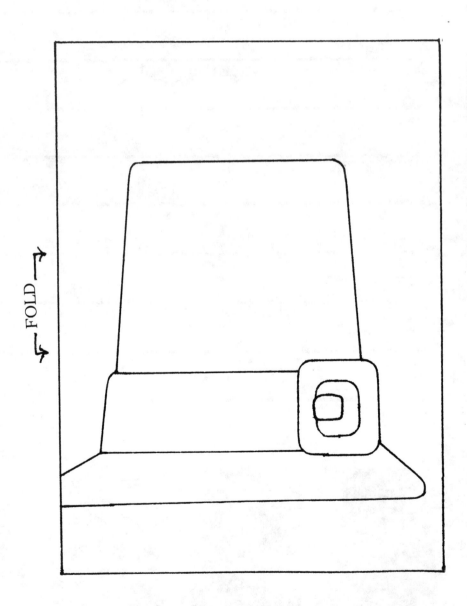

FOLD

RAVEN BORDER

These charming ravens will bring life to your fall bulletin board.

See page 9 for directions.

FOLD

Pur-r-fect Penmanship

NOVEMBER

There once was a turkey named Goon
Who thought he was born on the moon.
He'd float in the air,
Without ever a care
From evening until about noon.

Then quickly he'd land on the ground
Without even making a sound.
His thin legs would wobble,
He'd let out a gobble.
For the air he would leave with a bound.

But then one November he blew it.
He came to earth before he knew it.
And the fat, feathered beast
Was the Thanksgiving feast.
And that was all there was to it!

WORD WIZARD

1. November
2. chilly
3. Veterans Day
4. Pilgrim
5. turkey
6. **Mayflower**
7. wishbone
8. colony
9. cranberries
10. Indians
11. Thanksgiving
12. bleak
13. pumpkin pie
14. feast
15. harvest
16. cornstalk
17. snow flurries
18. deer
19. friends
20. settler
21. New World
22. parade
23. cornucopia
24. prayer
25. Massachusetts
26. thankful
27. fish
28. dinner
29. sharing
30. horn of plenty

TRICK THE TURKEY

DIRECTIONS: Choose a partner. Shuffle the game cards and place them face down on board. Each player puts a marker on start. Flip a penny. If it lands on heads, move marker ahead one space and draw a card. Hand it to your opponent. He will ask you to spell the word. If you do so correctly, stay where you are. If not, go back one space. If you flip tails, advance two and stay there if you spell the word correctly. If not, go back two spaces. Winner will be the first player to reach the end. Place all game cards at bottom of pile after use.

November	chilly	Veterans Day
Pilgrim	turkey	Mayflower
wishbone	colony	cranberries
Indians	Thanksgiving	bleak
pumpkin pie	feast	harvest
cornstalk	snow flurries	deer
friends	settler	New World
parade	cornucopia	prayer
Massachusetts	thankful	fish
dinner	sharing	horn of plenty

A BOASTFUL ROASTFULL

Turkey 1:

> I'm the best little turkey on the Arnett farm,
> And I've got wit and I've got charm.
> Mr. Arnett loves me the most, you see —
> So he'll never make a Thanksgiving dinner out of me!

Turkeys:

> Now you just wait until you get tall —
> After the winter, spring, summer and fall.
> Then Mr. Arnett will come after you
> And we will all bid you adieu.
> By then your feathers will be long;
> Those skinny legs so fat and strong;
> That belly of yours will be plump and round;
> We'll see it sagging to the ground;
> Those wings you flap into the air
> Will soon be sturdy and not so bare;
> And by your gobble we all will know
> You'll be the next one of us to go.

Turkey 1:

> Why do you worry about me so?
> It will be awhile before I grow
> Into the robust toms and hens
> That strut around here in Mr. Arnett's pens.

Mrs. Arnett:

> Now what's all this fuss about
> That seems to stop when I come out?
> There's plenty of corn for you to eat.
> I'll scatter it here around your feet.

I'll fatten you up from beak to tail
So none of you will be small and frail.
I'll show my husband your legs don't wobble
As you strut around with your gobble, gobble, gobble.

Turkey 1:

All of the seasons here quickly passed by —
And off the ground I fly so high.
My body is tiny, but trim and sturdy
And like I've said, "I'm the best little birdie!"
Mr. Arnett likes me most of all,
Even though I'm a little bit small.
I eat a lot and don't gain any weight
So I'll never end up on a Thanksgiving plate.

Turkeys:

You think that you are quite a fellow
'Cause your body is tiny and your feathers bright yellow;
You tilt your head as if to say,
"Please step aside and clear the way,
For I'm the greatest in the Arnett pens
Of all you turkeys and gobbling hens."

Mr. Arnett:

Now I've heard you turkeys for quite awhile
Complain and brag about your style.
And I've heard that one of you turkeys here
Seems to have nothing at all to fear.
So I've chosen the turkey who likes to boast
To be the one that I want for my Thanksgiving roast.

FINGER PUPPETS

to use with the CHORAL READING "A Boastful Roastfull." Make several big turkeys.

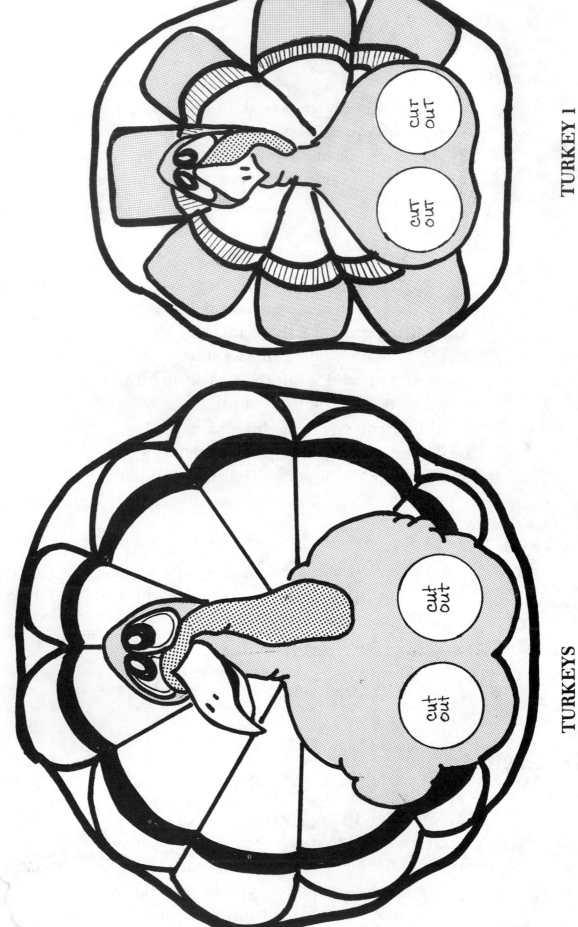

TURKEY 1

TURKEYS

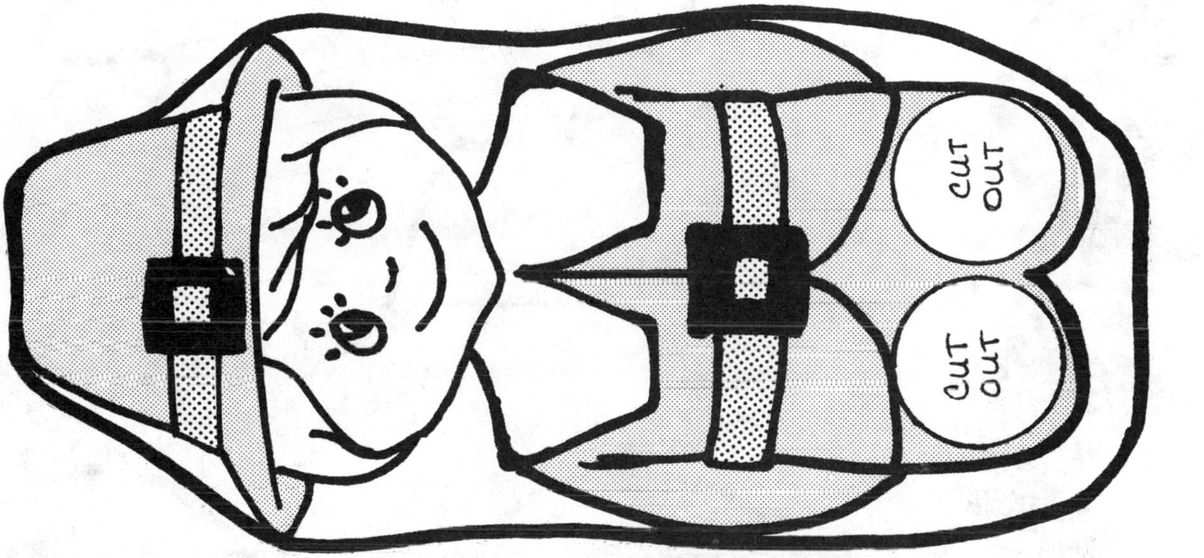

Mr. Arnett

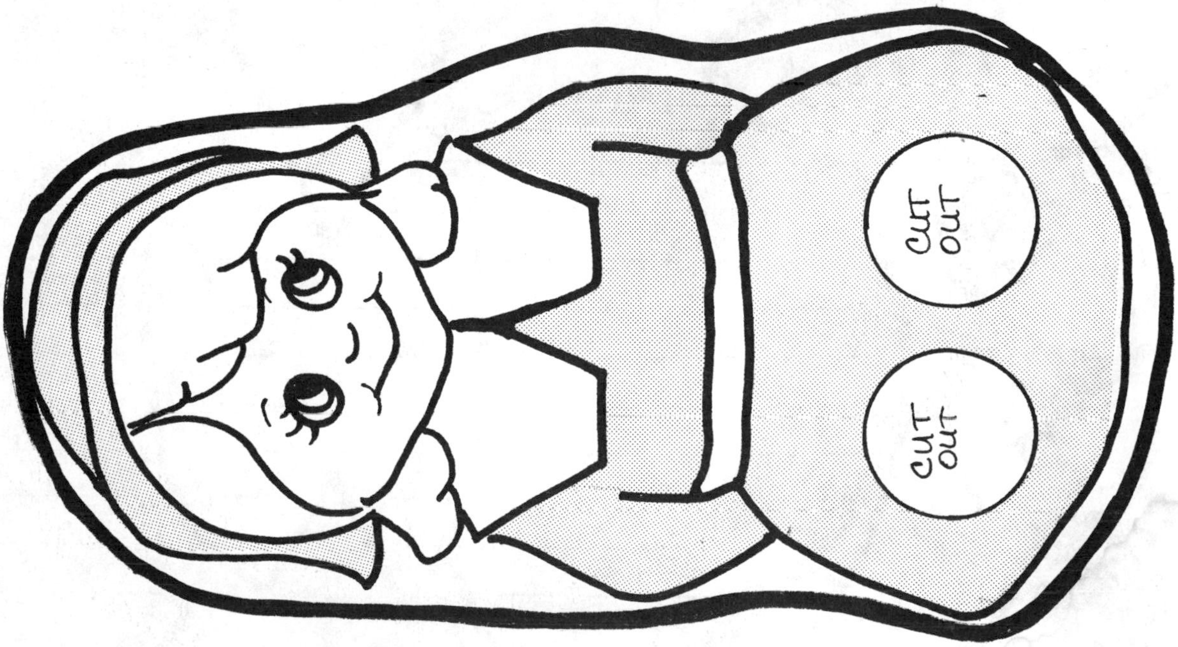

Mrs. Arnett

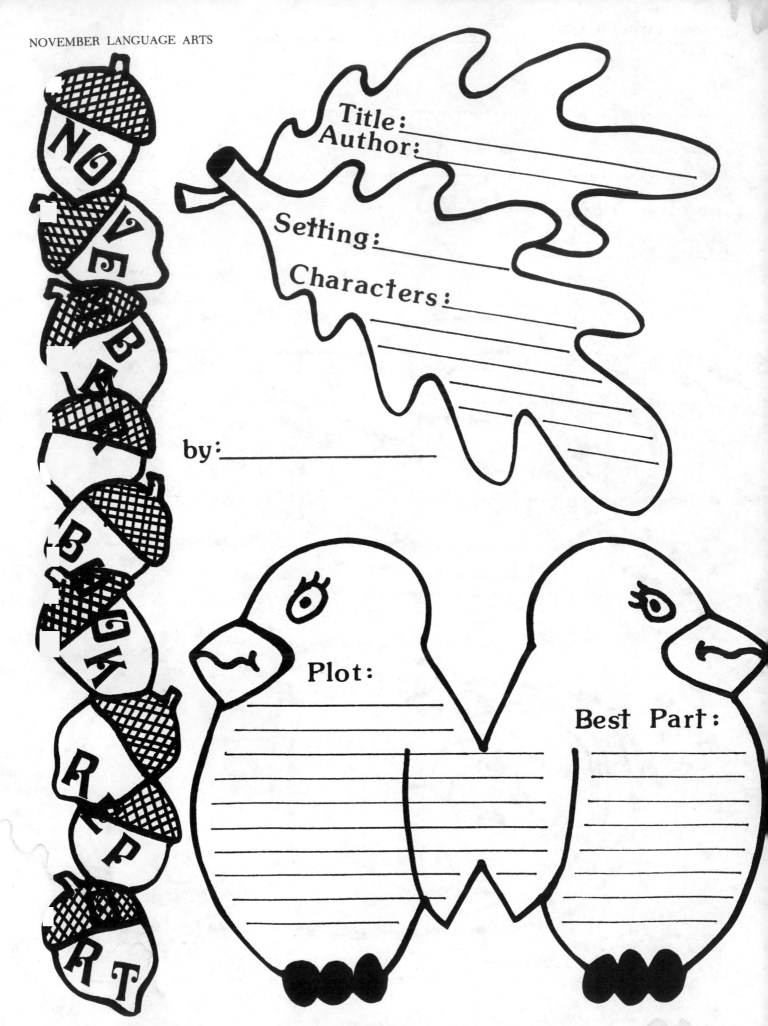

Title:
Author:

Setting:

Characters:

by:

Plot:

Best Part:

Date

TURKEY TRIPLETS

A three-line poem is called a TRIPLET. You will notice that all of the words at the end of each line rhyme.

Carefully read each of the TRIPLETS below and study the rhyme patterns. Then try to write a few of your own. Try to keep the number of beats in each line the same.

A Thanksgiving feast with turkey and dressing
And who knows what else (Mom keeps us guessing)
We gather together and share our blessing.

Old Tom Turkey sat by the gate
Along came Grandpa — he couldn't wait
To find a gobbler for my Thanksgiving plate.

A turkey and hen went out to play
But they forgot it was Thanksgiving Day
So in the oven they had to stay!

TRIM THE TURKEY

Name: _____

$\begin{array}{r}11\\\times 0\\\hline\end{array}$

$\begin{array}{r}634\\-122\\\hline\end{array}$

$\begin{array}{r}595\\-431\\\hline\end{array}$

$\begin{array}{r}43\\+19\\\hline\end{array}$

$\begin{array}{r}9\\\times 2\\\hline\end{array}$

$\begin{array}{r}2\\\times 1\\\hline\end{array}$

$\begin{array}{r}8\\8\\+12\\\hline\end{array}$

$\begin{array}{r}4\\\times 4\\\hline\end{array}$

$\begin{array}{r}769\\-431\\\hline\end{array}$

$\begin{array}{r}613\\+161\\\hline\end{array}$

$\begin{array}{r}437\\-121\\\hline\end{array}$

$\begin{array}{r}11\\+11\\\hline\end{array}$

$\begin{array}{r}14\\\times 1\\\hline\end{array}$

$\begin{array}{r}619\\-407\\\hline\end{array}$

$\begin{array}{r}49\\-31\\\hline\end{array}$

$\begin{array}{r}2\\\times 2\\\hline\end{array}$

$\begin{array}{r}48\\+18\\\hline\end{array}$

$\begin{array}{r}461\\+431\\\hline\end{array}$

$\begin{array}{r}635\\-431\\\hline\end{array}$

$\begin{array}{r}64\\+28\\\hline\end{array}$

$\begin{array}{r}19\\+19\\\hline\end{array}$

$\begin{array}{r}8\\\times 1\\\hline\end{array}$

To trim this turkey, solve each problem. Use the code here to color the picture.

If the last digit of the answer ends in this number, color the picture as follows:

0 Green   **2** Red   **4** Brown   **6** Yellow   **8** Orange

Hunting for Something?

As you solve the problems, color your answers in the spaces below.

1. 724
   -385

2. 810
   -367

3. 955
   -496

4. 511
   -193

5. 600
   -475

6. 407
   -388

7. 916
   -749

8. 624
   -587

9. 524
   -395

10. 843
   -576

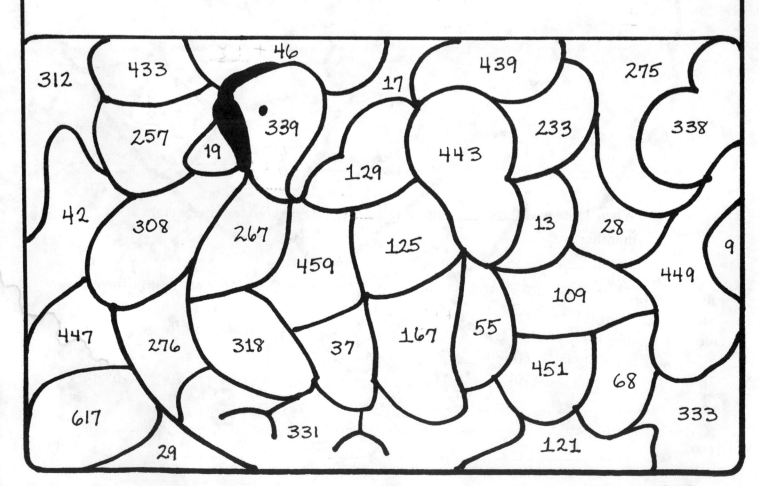

Weight Gained by Tillie Turkey

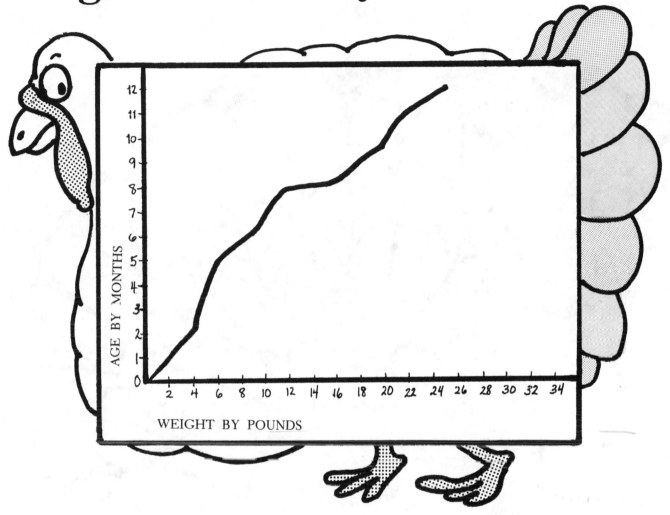

1. When Tillie was one month old she weighed _____ pounds.
2. Tillie weighed 7 pounds when she was _____ months old.
3. At four months Tillie weighed about _____ pounds.
4. When Tillie was _____ months old she weighed about half her weight at 12 months.
5. At _____ months Tillie gained about 4 pounds.
6. When Tillie was 2 months old, she weighed 4 pounds. How old was Tillie when she doubled this weight? _____
7. This graph shows Tillie's weight until she is _____ months old.
8. At 24 pounds, Tillie is _____ months old.
9. How many months did it take Tillie to gain from 18 pounds to 22 pounds? _____
10. During what months does Tillie's weight double her age? _____

_____

This will be your cover for a booklet. Color it brightly, cut it out, and staple your other sheets behind it. Be sure your name is on the front.

TURKEY TIME

How's Your Turkey Dressing?

Follow these directions to complete your picture.
Use the space below.

1. Draw grass across the bottom of this page.
2. Draw a large turkey in the center.
3. Add a Pilgrim hat to the turkey.
4. Put glasses on your turkey.
5. Design clothes for your turkey to wear.
6. Add shoes to his feet.
7. Draw a background for your picture and color everything.

Green Bean Grammar

As you read each sentence, identify these parts of speech by using the symbols shown above. Some words will not be marked.

Example: Virginia will make delicious salad for Thanksgiving.

1. Suddenly the big fat turkey gobbled.

2. He ran and petted the two hens.

3. We ate with them on Thanksgiving Day.

4. Slowly the turkey roasted in Grandma's oven.

5. I love pumpkin pie with whipped cream.

6. A male turkey is called a tom.

7. That football game was played in the new stadium.

8. Dad and Kim will watch the parade later.

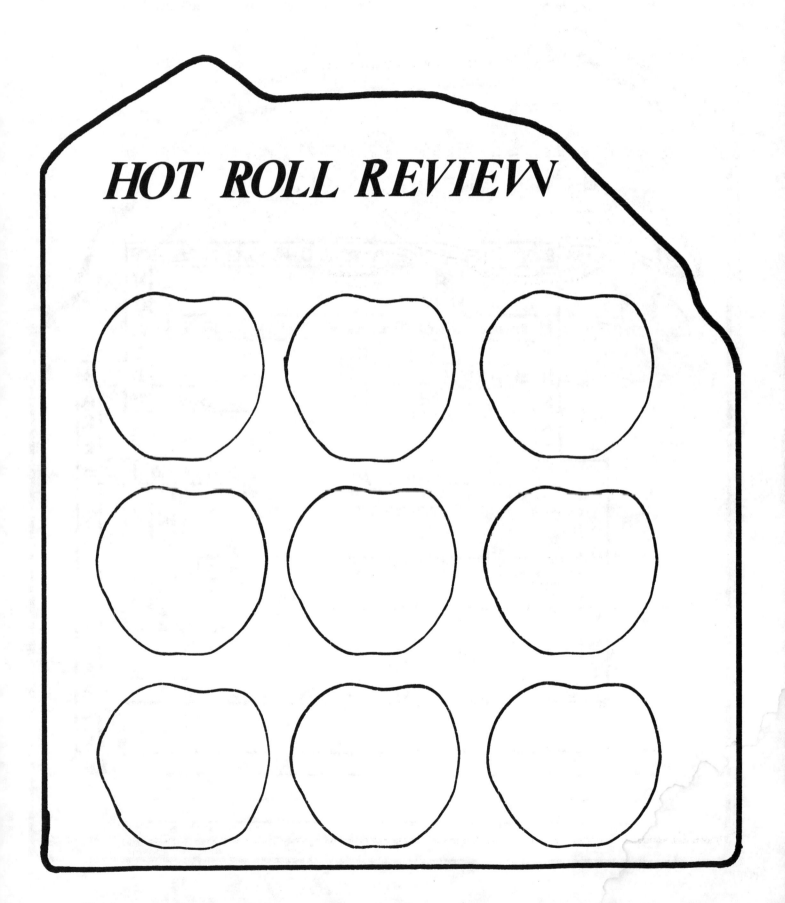

HOT ROLL REVIEW

Follow the maze to find a secret message. Write that message on the lines below.

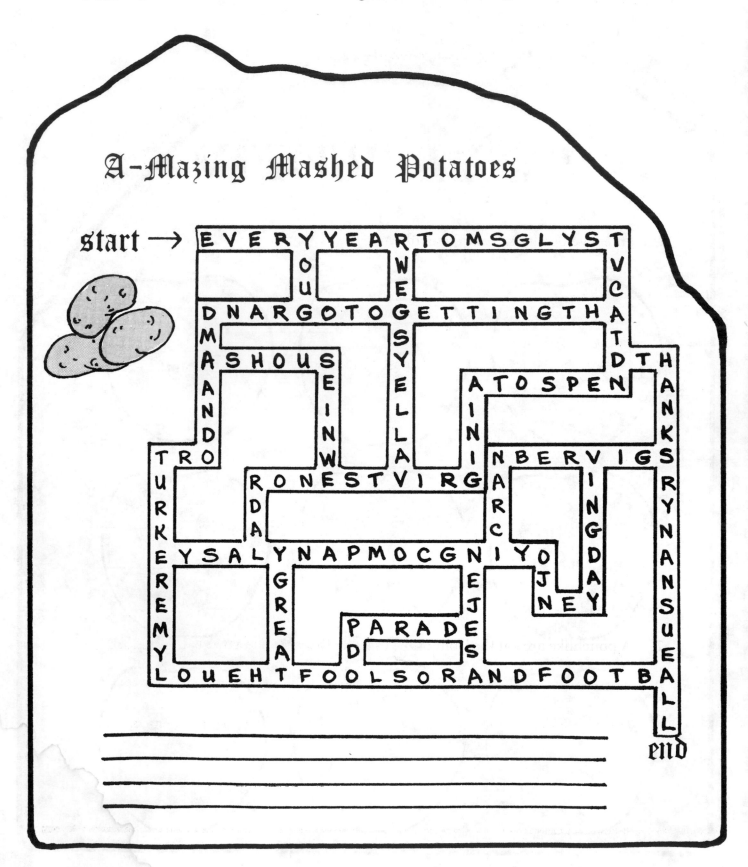

A-Mazing Mashed Potatoes

start →

_____

_____

_____

_____

TURKEY TRIVIA

Use an encyclopedia to find these answers.

1. A male turkey is called a _____ and the female is called

   a _____.

2. Five states which produce the most turkeys are:

   _____.

3. The name for a young turkey is _____.

4. Wild turkeys eat _____.

5. Some ways male turkeys are different from the females include: _____

   _____.

6. Turkey eggs are usually a _____ color.

7. A pouchlike area at the front of the turkey's throat is known as a _____.

8. The adult male turkey is about _____ feet long.

9. Wild turkeys were served by the _____ on the first Thanksgiving

   Day.

Under each pie tell what fractional part is shaded. Then circle each numerator!

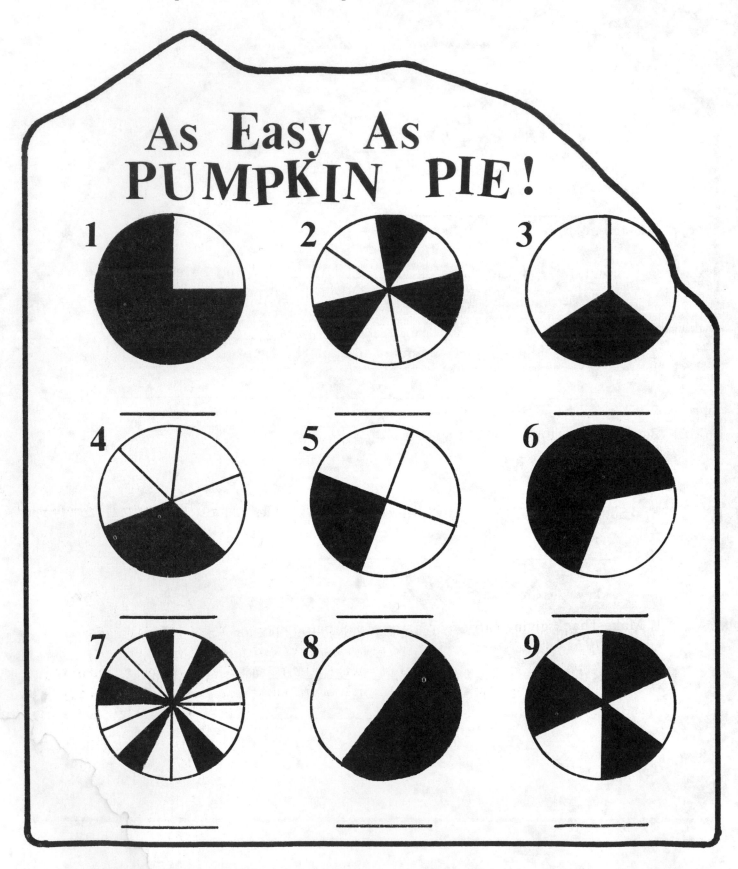

As Easy As PUMPKIN PIE !

1

2

3

4

5

6

7

8

9

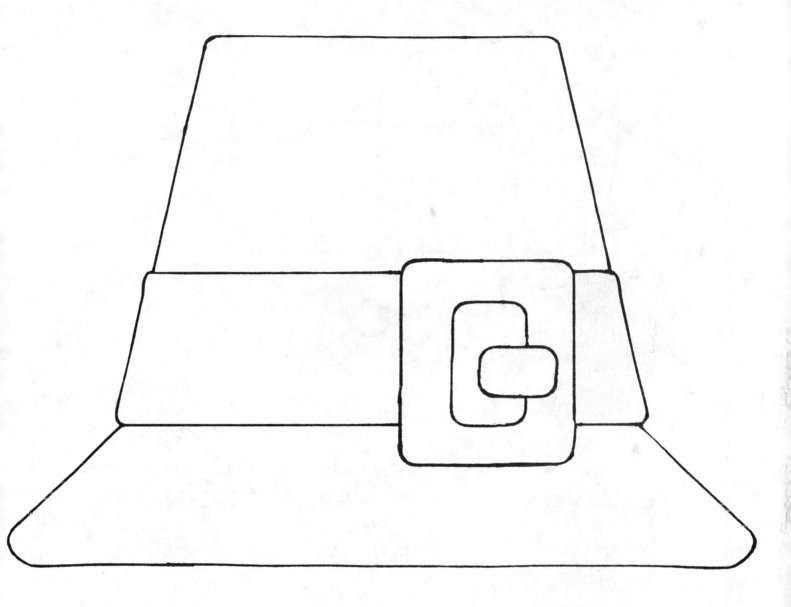

Suggestions:
1. Make Thanksgiving cards by placing top of hat along fold of construction paper. Use a light colored paper so that verse on inside is visible.
2. Make several hats. Across the top of each write the name of a category. Have children list on paper words which fit into the themes or categories. Use this as a station.

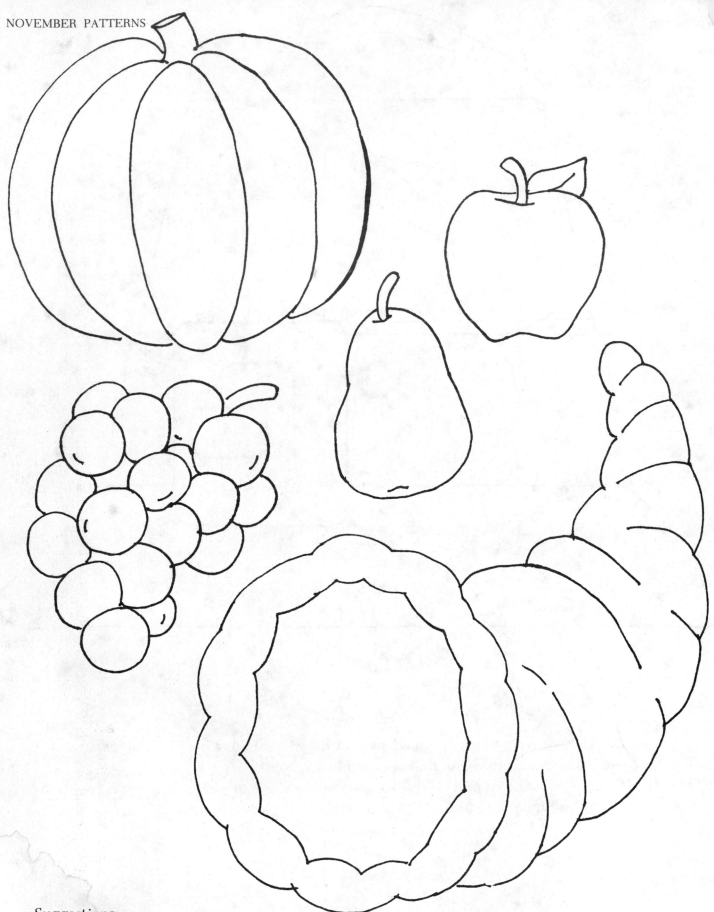

Suggestions:
1. Use as a ditto for children to cut out and assemble. Use as a booklet cover.
2. Use as a ditto on heavy paper. This will form a base for a torn paper mosaic art lesson.

Suggestions:

1. Use as a ditto for a coloring contest.
2. Use as ditto for a puppet play. Mount cardboard girl on stick.

Suggestions:
1. Use as a ditto for a coloring contest.
2. Use as a ditto for a puppet play. Mount cardboard boy on stick.

Suggestions:
1. Use as a ditto for a color sheet or booklet cover of November work.
2. Use as a puppet in a play with Pilgrim boy and girl. Mount cardboard turkey on stick.

Suggestions:

1. Write math problem on each acorn to use as mini work sheet in a math center.
2. Write scrambled sentences on acorns for children to unscramble. (You may want them to add punctuation also if it is not given.)

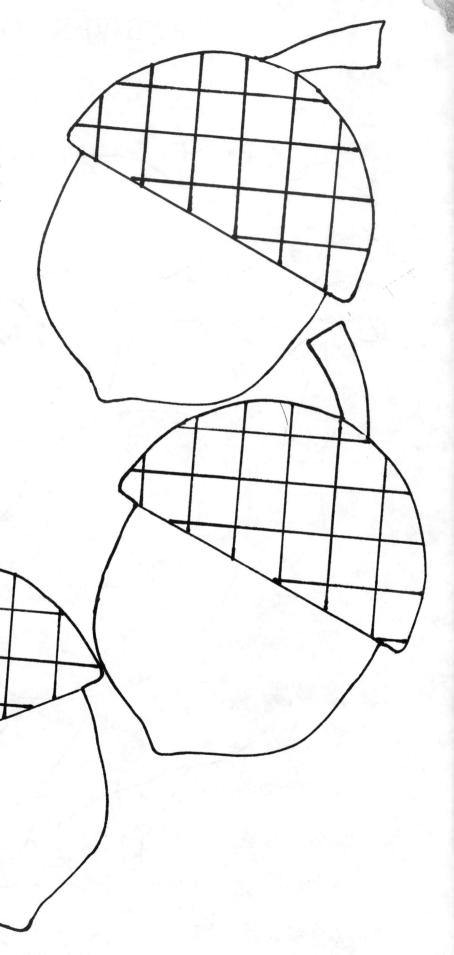

ANSWER KEY

Page 19
1. 3 years
2. Jeremy, 37
3. Jeremy, Dave, Dave
4. Matt
5. 1982 and 1983
6. Jeremy and Adam, 2
7. 37
8. 1981
9. 8
10. 106

Page 54

Across:
1. Halloween
3. boo
7. hat
10. odor
12. twitchin'
13. haggardy
15. windy
16. seeks
18. crested
19. sill
21. frazzle
22. cauldron
23. witch

Down:
1. haunted
2. door
4. ghouly
5. stairs
6. crimson
8. scurry
9. silhouette
11. dangle
14. skull
15. web
17. spiders
20. brew

Page 55
1. spiders
2. one day every year
3. evening
4. on her back
5. nose
6. spiders' legs, bat wings, cats, blood, skull
7. crimson
8. the odor makes her sick
9. cat and hat
10. next Halloween

Page 59
1. = 7,092
2. = 8,236
3. = 12,140
4. = 8,448
5. = 11,325
6. = 13,400
7. = 7,080
8. = 11,678

Page 62
1. 24 people
2. 18 cupcakes
3. 36 pieces of candy
4. 164 pages
5. $1.50
6. 58 years old
7. $5.76

Page 65

Columbus was an explorer who discovered America in 1492.

Page 105

Green:	$8 \times 5 = 40$	
Red:	$4 \times 8 = 32$	
	$3 \times 4 = 12$	
	$11 \times 2 = 22$	
	$9 \times 8 = 72$	
	$6 \times 2 = 12$	
	$12 \times 11 = 132$	
	$6 \times 7 = 42$	
Brown:	$11 \times 4 = 44$	
	$8 \times 3 = 24$	
	$6 \times 4 = 24$	
	$7 \times 2 = 14$	
	$8 \times 8 = 64$	

Yellow:	$6 \times 6 = 36$
	$12 \times 8 = 96$
	$8 \times 7 = 56$
Orange:	$7 \times 4 = 28$
	$11 \times 8 = 88$
	$12 \times 9 = 108$
	$3 \times 6 = 18$
	$2 \times 4 = 8$
	$8 \times 6 = 48$

Page 106
1. 339
2. 443
3. 459
4. 318
5. 125
6. 19
7. 167
8. 37
9. 129
10. 267

Page 107
1. 2 pounds
2. 5½ months old
3. 5 pounds
4. 8 months
5. 8 months
6. 6 months
7. 12 months
8. 11½ months
9. 2 months
10. 1, 2, 9, 10, 11

Page 109

Page 112

1. Suddenly the big fat turkey gobbled.

2. He ran and pecked the two hens.

3. We ate with them on Thanksgiving Day

4. Slowly the turkey roasted in Grandma's oven.

5. I love pumpkin pie with whipped cream.

6. A male turkey is called a tom.

7. That football game was played in the new stadium.

8. Dad and Kim will watch the parade later.

Page 114

Every year we go to Grandma's house in West Virginia to spend Thanksgiving Day enjoying company, great food, parades, and football.

Page 115

1. tom, hen
2. California, Minnesota, Virginia, Iowa, Texas
3. poult
4. nuts, seeds, berries, insects, small fruits
5. A male turkey: 1) has long tuft of bristles on chest; 2) has spurs on legs; 3) has no feathers on neck or head; 4) is larger than the female; 5) is a brighter color
6. tan with brown speckles
7. wattle
8. 4
9. Pilgrims

Page 116

1. ③4   6. ②3
2. ③8   7. ⑤16
3. ①3   8. ①2
4. ②6   9. ③6
5. ①4

124